Suicide:
Intervention and Therapy

• • •

Undoing the Forever Decision

DR. PAUL G. QUINNETT

Classic Publishing • Spokane, WA

Printed in the United States

Classic Publishing
Spokane, Washington

Cover Design by James Quinnett
Layout by Peggy Robideaux

Library of Congress Cataloging-in-Publication Data

Quinnett, Paul G., 1939-
    Suicide: Intervention and Therapy

    1. Suicide. 2. Suicide—Prevention. 3. Suicide—
Psychological Aspects. I. Title

ISBN 1-879331-28-4

Disclaimer

The author and the publisher wish the reader to know that this book is for educational and training purposes only. Application of any of these materials to any case or cases is the sole responsibility of the individual practitioner, counselor, or agency.

• • •

The identities of the people written about in this book have been carefully disguised in accordance with professional standards of confidentiality and in keeping with their rights to privileged communication with the author.

TABLE OF CONTENTS

PART III

Emergency phone numbers, resource people, referral information, and backups.

Author's Note

. . .

This book was written especially for the crisis volunteer, counselor, minister, school teacher, social worker, therapist, law enforcement officer, clergyman, physician, nurse, alcohol or drug counselor, and all other professional or paraprofessional human service workers who—while not suicide experts—come into contact with suicidal people. It was also written for those who work with suicidal patients in therapy.

This book is not comprehensive. It is not research oriented *per se*, but the recommendations for action are based upon a blend of the current literature as well as the author's 25 years of experience in the field of mental health, substance abuse, psychotherapy, and suicidology. The perspective is both professional and personal and, as such, should not be construed as the last word on the only way to do things. For more detailed study of suicide intervention and treatment, a list of readings has been included.

My emphasis here is on the practical. For information to be helpful, it has to be easy to access and use—thus the brevity and layout of the text. I've kept psychological jargon to a minimum and tried to focus less on epidemiology, statistics, and theory and more on what each of us can do to save a life. I've tried to condense a great deal of information into small, relevant packages and, as a result, documentation of sources has been less than perfect. Considering the stakes, however, I believe this to be a good trade off.

Suicide is the most complicated of all human behavior, and preventing suicide remains both a mystery and a challenge. Even the language of suicide is expressed quite differently by people of different ages, sexes, and ethnicities and, while much of what we can do to save lives is generic, we also need to be sensitized to a variety of unique needs, modes of expression, cultural differences, and special problems faced by different people at different times over the life span. Where I've been able, I've tried to touch on many of these special subjects in the final section of the book.

Last, because working with suicidal people is so very stressful, where I can I've tried to lighten the load each of us has offered to share with a bit of humor. Such humor is not meant to be disrespectful to suicidal people; rather, it is meant to help make this work possible at all.

How to Use This Book

• • •

For ready use, this text is divided into three sections: Intervention, Treatment, and Special Topics.

Intervention

The first section has been laid out along the basic theoretical idea that suicide is a process—not a fixed event. Simply put, what this means is that at the time you first come into contact with someone who is contemplating suicide, you may be meeting that person at either end of what I'll call the suicide journey.

The suicide journey begins with the simple idea that maybe killing oneself would solve some problem or other and ends, sometimes, with a completed suicide. This journey can be a short, swift one, but it is more likely a long and labored one. Where you meet someone along this tortured road is all important.

For example, if you're the first person to learn about the first passive suicide thought a never-before-suicidal young person has ever had, your job shouldn't be too tough. However, if you meet an old, white, alcoholic, failed accountant under indictment for tax evasion who has a previous suicide attempt history and who has just learned his wife is leaving him next Friday, you may be meeting someone whose journey toward suicide is nearly ended.

How we respond to each of these travelers (and how they respond to our interventions) is critical to helping them survive. The first part of this book, therefore, deals with the various stages of suicidality, its assessment, and the range of possible interventions available to us.

Every suicidal person I've met takes roughly the same journey. The back roads, highways, and detours vary, but everyone who kills him- or herself must begin with the notion, move on to active contemplation, make a plan and, before taking the final action, generally communicate his or her intention to die to others. This communication will vary from verbal threats to gestures to silent behavioral clues to lethal attempts, but most people will signal they are nearing the end of their journey. And while there are exceptions to this troubled route, the vast majority of sufferers travel the one I've just described.

How to meet these travelers, what questions to ask, and what actions to take to keep them safe are written in the form of procedures that can be adapted to local resources and state laws. There are no doubt other ways to do this intervention work, but these are the ways that have worked for me.

Treatment, Management, and Therapy

The second part of the book is for therapists, counselors, and clinicians who work with suicidal people. As such, this portion of the book deals with all the many ways we can use ourselves, our training, and our therapeutic relationships to help weary travelers not only pass over a stretch of bad road, but enjoy the journey of life to its natural end.

As there are several problems inherent in ourselves as helpers, our clients, and the systems in which we work, I've tried to address these as well.

Special Topics

The third part of the book amounts to exploded views of subjects that not everyone needs to know. But if you are working with a certain type of person or problem or have a special need, this section can give you a bit more depth and background. For example, if you are a school official who has just experienced a student suicide, you may wish to explore procedures for containing the crisis and preventing further suicidal behavior in other children. You can turn directly to the alphabetically arranged information that looks most helpful.

Suicide Prevention Support System

On the last page of the book I have listed those agencies, hospitals, mental health centers, possible supervisors, consultants, and others who, once you have filled in their names and phone numbers, should provide you a kind of personalized support network. Once completed per your community and personal choices, you may wish to carry some of these numbers with you at all times.

Last, please be reminded that what we don't know about suicide could fill books. Therefore, don't be too disappointed if you don't find everything you need here. But, where I know a resource or book or an association or phone number that might prove helpful, I've included them in the relevant text.

1   • • •

Intervention

Getting Started

Let's assume something from the start: You have already made contact with someone suicidal, or at least someone who, in your judgment, may be thinking about suicide. You may now assume two things: 1) The situation may or may not be serious and, 2) You're on the hook to do something.

The first rule of suicide intervention is to *do something*. Don't worry about doing something wrong; it's doing nothing that gets people killed. Since the potentially suicidal person you're dealing with is still with us, at least a part of him or her wants to live. Trust me on this: The part that wants to live is much more forgiving of our mistakes as interventionists and therapists than you can ever imagine. So, go ahead. Take the first step.

Step One: If the question, "Is this person possibly suicidal?," is already in your head, it is very likely already in the head of the person you're worried about. Therefore, if in doubt, *ask*. Just cut the tension and ask:

"You look pretty upset; are you thinking of hurting yourself?" or, "Have you been thinking about suicide?" or, "Have you ever wanted to stop living?" or, "Are you thinking about killing yourself?"

There are many ways to ask this critical question and you may come up with one that suits you better than any of these. In my experience, most any question that goes right to the heart of the matter will work, especially if it is age, race, and ethnic sensitive.

There is, however, one way to *not* ask the question. And that is, "You're not thinking of suicide, are you?"

Framing the question so as to encourage a negative reply closes the door on the suicidal person and says, in effect, "Please don't burden me with your troubles." People who ask the question in this form are, most likely, frightened they may get a positive answer. And a positive answer, as everyone knows who has ever worked with anyone contemplating suicide, means you have now assumed at least some responsibility to help save a life.

The best outcome to the are-you-thinking-of-suicide question is that person feels immediate relief that someone noticed the pain and cared enough to ask about that pain. The result can be the beginning of a life-saving relationship.

The worst outcome is that the person is not suicidal and now feels you've asked a stupid, even intrusive question. This is too bad, but okay. In this business, stupid questions can save lives. All you need do is apologize and move on. In my experience, it's the unasked questions that lead to tragedy.

Note: Since many hints and threats of suicide are coded and sometimes difficult to interpret, it is better to be bold and blunt than shy and sorry. (See Clues to Suicide in the Special Topics section for more details.)

STEP TWO: Now that you know the person you're talking to is suicidal, the question, is *how suicidal?* This is an assessment question, and while I will deal more with assessment in the next section, it is important at this point to answer only a couple of more questions:

* Does this person want to die in the next ten minutes, or can this suicide business wait a little bit? and,
* Can we talk?

If the answer to these questions are yes and yes (we can wait and talk), then we have a little time and there's no need to push the panic button. Most people who have been asked if they've been thinking about suicide are quite willing to talk. In fact, they've been wanting to talk to someone for weeks, months or even years—which is why, if you've just confirmed your fears that someone is suicidal, it's a good idea to have at least an hour available to begin the listening process.

It is well to remember that the great majority of suicidal people human service workers come into contact with are *not* going to kill themselves in the next ten minutes. Tomorrow, next Friday at noon, by the end of the month, someday... but not right now. Imminently suicidal people—those who are in a high state of arousal and agitation as they approach some final, savage act—are rarely seen outside of emergency rooms, or while being evaluated by police, acute care mental health professionals, and/or paramedic personnel. Such episodes of imminent suicidality last only minutes, not hours or days.

Again, if in doubt about how urgent the person is to die, simply ask more questions. Only by asking more questions can you reach the level of comfort you need to continue to be helpful.

STEP THREE: Now that we have an agreement to wait and talk, we need an agreement to accomplish two other vital things:

• Create a safe environment so that,

• We can learn something about the problem that suicide would solve.

To create a safe environment simply means to remove any means of self-harm the person may be carrying or have nearby. This means asking for and getting any knives, razors, guns, pills, and such the person may have in his/her immediate possession. If you're already communicating out a ten-story window with someone who wants to jump, talking the person inside to talk is the way to a safe environment. So is convincing someone to put down a gun, or put it on a desk so you can pick it up and put it in a safe place (touch guns only if you're familiar with firearms), or to hand over razors and knives.

Note: Putting yourself at risk (although the risk may be low) is never recommended. Suicidal people are rarely homicidal, but accidents can happen, so why take chances?

If the means of suicide are at home, getting an agreement to dispose of them is essential. This can sometimes be quite difficult, but it must be done. In fact, sometimes a safe environment cannot be achieved until a good, therapeutic relationship has been established—in which case (and if involuntary interventions are not possible) we just have to do the best we can and keep working toward this goal. To leave a person in possession of the means of suicide can be, in a dark mood, interpreted by the suicidal person as an indication the helper didn't really care, e.g., "If Sharon really cared she wouldn't have let me keep my pills."

˗ Telephone work, by the way, is the most difficult; therefore, if you can't get a commitment to a safe environment, feel free to up the ante. When a person on the phone cannot, will not, and/or refuses to agree to safety after a few minutes of your best efforts to get a commitment (and you feel the risk is high), start a trace, send in the police, paramedics, or mental health professionals. You can't reach down a phone line and remove the gun, nor can you tell (with any reliability) when and how many pills someone has taken. If in doubt, reach out.

Most of those who complain you've violated their privacy by sending in a third party and who, as a result, threaten to sue you, won't. After all, they called you, you didn't call them. Then too, they have to prove to a judge and jury that you harmed them in some way by violating their privacy, and that isn't very likely when you are clearly a good-hearted, well-intentioned human being (which you are).

STEP FOUR: Whether you've got a safe environment or not, here are several things to do to get a life-saving relationship going. The reason to get a relationship going is straightforward: You want to keep the person alive long enough to find out what suicide would accomplish. Here's how to get a suicidal person talking:

- Pay perfect attention. Good rapport is nothing more than feeling paid attention to. Don't butt in. Say to yourself, "listen..., listen.... learn."

- Remain calm and talk about suicide openly...as if you did it everyday. The suicidal person is desperate to find someone who is calm, warm, and collected—someone who doesn't frighten easily and isn't put off by suicide talk. You're it.

- Don't condemn the idea of suicide, but don't praise it either. Accept it as an interesting option but, possibly, too much of a solution to whatever problem is at hand.

- Normalize feelings—especially feelings of panic and/or feeling overwhelmed.

- State plainly that you're going to be there to help the person through whatever mess he or she is in. Just say it: "I'm here. I'll help you out of this."

- If you feel a platitude like "I know exactly how you feel" or "You'll feel better in the morning" or any other bumper-sticker slogan about to roll off your tongue— bite it! (Your tongue, that is.) Platitudes don't play well with suicidal people and those experiencing severe psychological pain. If the easy stuff worked, suicidal people wouldn't be talking to you.

- Don't be afraid to say you don't understand. Because you are talking to a suicidal person you can figure, right off, they don't feel understood. So never say you *do* understand unless you really do. And the only way you can be sure you do understand is to have that understanding confirmed by the person in the soup.

  Examples of good questions and probing statements include, "It sounds like your dad is really going to cream you when he finds out you've wrecked his car" or,

"From what you're saying, it doesn't seem like there's much hope she'll come back" or, "If you fail this course, does it mean your parents won't let you go on to college?" From them you will get either confirmations or non-confirmations. The more confirmations you get, the more you understand. And the more the suicidal person believes you understand, the better things will go.

Note: World's oldest safe assumption: Assume nothing!

In my experience, what most helps suicidal people who reveal their suicidality for the first time is an accepting, understanding, compassionate human reception to their felt suffering. An expression of unmistakable faith in a positive outcome also helps. But this optimism cannot be sophomoric, Pollyanish, or simpleminded. If the sufferer's problems were easily solved, they would have already been solved.

Therefore, the main message from you to the sufferer is this: "Yes, the situation is desperate, but it is not hopeless. Something *can* be done and something *will* be done!" You can cement this good faith offer with the assurance that, "No matter how rough things get, *we're* going to get through this *together*." If you get even a weak, little smile, or sigh of relief, or anything like an agreement to put off what seemed inevitable before the bond between the two of you was formed, then you can consider your mission mostly accomplished.

STEP FIVE: Now relax. You're doing fine. The intervention job is almost done. We've got the beginnings of a life-saving relationship and the only thing left to do is to take care of some loose ends.

Depending on the quality of the connection you've just made, the risk of an imminent act of self-destruction is immediately reduced. Just *how much reduced* is the greatest puzzle in suicidology today and, from a personal and professional perspective, the single most nagging question ever invented. But, in my view, there's no point in losing perfectly good sleep over this failure of science. Instead, let's just do what we can.

With the breathing space you've established (we've got a safe environment, time to learn about the problems, and a tentative agreement from the suicidal person to stick around long enough to see what can be done), here's how to put in the insurance.

• *Get some help.* Basically, this means sharing the knowledge that the person you've been working with has expressed a wish to die. The wish may be strong or weak. You may not know how "at risk" the person is. You may, in fact, be in the referral business and your job is simply to identify the fact of *some* suicide risk and make sure someone better trained or more experienced than yourself is going to make a more in-depth determination.

   The findings from this more thorough determination/consultation will determine your course of action as regards any need for treatment—in or out of a hospital.

• *Get others involved.* As above, these "others" may be colleagues, supervisors, or consultants. If the person has a family available, give careful consideration to letting them know one of their loved ones is contemplating self-destruction. Parents of young people need to know their child is in trouble (in some states, when a child is under a certain age, the laws require disclosure of such matters).

Note: Notifying other people depends on several dicey matters: the suicidal person's wishes, the laws of confidentiality, your school's or agency's rules about disclosure, the age of the person, etc.. However, you should *never promise to keep a suicidal person's status a secret.* To be drawn into such an agreement puts you both at risk.

Sometimes the reason a person wants to suicide is to hurt someone else. Make sure contacting this "someone else" is not going to make the problem worse.

To get others involved, ask the suicidal person who he or she would like to know about the crisis. Then ask permission to get in touch with that person(s). Once the network of communication has been expanded, move on to the survival plan.

• *Make a survival plan:* The best plans are simple ones. For someone who is not going to the hospital, a good plan includes the following elements: safety, phone access, and clear instructions for what to do if a crisis develops.

1) *Safety:* Make sure the person is going to be safe. This means arranging for someone who genuinely cares about the person to be immediately available— preferably under the same roof. It also means someone responsible has removed all the means of suicide in the place of residence (guns, pills, etc.). Not always, but sometimes, suicide is an impulsive act, especially among the young. A safe plan removes temptations.

2) *Phone access:* Give the suicidal person (and whoever is going to be part of the survival plan) at least three telephone numbers (on the last page of this book). These should include the local crisis line, an

emergency room where immediate medical care can be gotten, your office, and a backup number where you can be reached. Everyone knows 911, but many folks are reluctant to use it. It's your call about giving out your home number, but the more personal the connection, the better. The main thing is that, since you've built a life-saving bridge to the suicidal person, he or she must know the bridge is there, open, and easy to cross.

3) *Crisis Instructions:* Give clear instructions on how to get to the nearest hospital or mental health crisis team in the event something breaks down. The law of unforeseen consequences (if things can go wrong, they will) seems to operate in overtime with suicidal people. Again, *assume nothing.*

With a safe, secure, easily accessed and directed survival plan in place, the only thing left to do is to get a commitment for continuing counseling and/or treatment. This help may come from you, or it may come from someone you are going to refer the person to. While making good referrals is something of an art, make sure you've done at least the following:

• Have the name, number, time, and place of the person the suicidal person will see next. It is best if you can set this referral up while the person is still with you. If possible, have the suicidal person talk to the person on your phone while you are still together. Or, if the person is physically available, arrange to introduce the two of them and confirm the next appointment among the three of you. As a kind of safety net, this human connection is everything.

If you feel the person you've been working with is resistant to following through with the referral, either take the person to the appointment yourself, arrange for some significant other to take the person, or re-evaluate how bad things really are. More definitive action, e.g., hospitalization, may be required.

The No-Suicide Contract

One of the ways to confirm you have a commitment to stay alive is through the use of the No-Suicide Contract. Whether you are going to treat or counsel the person yourself, or make a referral to someone else, getting a No-Suicide Contract is often a test of how willing the person is to give life another try.

People are funny. They can be desperately suicidal and yet, given a chance to make a deal to stay alive, they'll take it. This deal, whatever form it takes, is often called the No-Suicide Contract. You generally ask for a No-Suicide Contract *after* you have built a relationship, not before.

Sometimes, after an hour or so of working with someone, you may feel you don't need to ask for a contract to stay alive after all. My advice, however, is to ask for the commitment anyway—if only to be sure you didn't misread the person and so that, if something awful happens, you'll be able to sleep nights knowing you left no stone unturned.

Some folks prefer to make a "no-harm" deal since many upset parasuicidal people (those whose suicidal behavior only looks like, sounds like, seems like suicide but rarely leads to death) will carve up their arms or take enough pills to get "just a good night's sleep." (See Special Topics section for more on parasuicidality.)

The elements of the contract basically involve the suicidal person agreeing to stay alive until some work (usually therapy, a family intervention, etc.) can be accomplished. It includes not only agreeing to stay safe and healthy, but includes a commitment to the future. Such a contract can be entered into with a simple verbal agreement:

> "Will you give me your word not to hurt yourself until we've had a chance to sort these problems out?"

or,

> "If we're going to work together, I need you to agree to stay alive. Will you do that?"

or, if a referral is being made,

> "Will you promise to stay safe until you see Ms. Wilson?"

For the vast majority of people, their word is their bond, and that will be enough. Getting a handshake *and* a promise is even better. As I've never been one who thought much of written agreements between us and the people who need us (feels too much like we don't trust each other and ought to have lawyers involved), I'll take a handshake and smile every time.

Note: It is a good idea to anticipate crises and, to make sure the person reaches out for you instead of a razor or a gun, have him or her agree to *talk* to you before doing anything rash. By asking that the person talk to you, not just call (e.g. leave a "call" with your answering service), the person implicitly agrees to a dialogue. It's dialogues that save lives, not messages left on voice mail.

Safety Means No Alcohol

Because alcohol plays such a major role in suicide (some reports suggest the majority of people who kill themselves are under the influence at the time they die), get an agreement to *not drink* until help is underway. Alcohol not only impairs social judgment, it clouds our ability to imagine the consequences of our acts, including suicidal ones. If we're depressed and/or angry, alcohol may provide short-term relief for these symptoms; however, alcohol may also enhance these feelings to intolerable levels. The direct psychological effect of alcohol in the bloodstream is far from predictable. As a result, and together with the increased impulsivity and "stinkin' thinkin'" alcohol can produce, highly lethal situations can develop very quickly.

Therefore, while the person you are working with may or may not be alcoholic, you do not have to make this diagnosis in order to ask for sobriety in your contract for safety. All by itself, a diagnosis never saved anyone; it's getting the booze out of the formula that greatly enhances the chances for survival. If the person is unable or unwilling to make a commitment to safety through sobriety, then more vigorous intervention may be necessary. (See Alcohol in Special Topics.)

Without setting a time limit, not-very-suicidal people will agree to stay alive without much of a fight. They'll shake your hand, nod, and promise to give themselves some time. Finding a sympathetic listener, they've already gotten at least some of the help they sought.

In other cases, the suicidal person will not agree to either safety or the future. Or, being cagey and resistant, the person will agree to only 24 hours. Or three days. Or a week. If you can get a month, things are not likely to be terribly desperate. But if you can't get a day, or a week, or enough time to see the referral person, or any sort of believable, good faith promise to stick around so others can help, then you may have someone who's so low on the hope scale that what he or she is really saying is: *"Thanks for listening, but I'm still going to kill myself."*

You may now push the panic button and go on to the next chapter.

2 ...

Second-Level Intervention

In the last section, the suicidal people we met were only just beginning the journey toward self destruction. Toying with the notion that death may be better than life, they were not greatly invested in dying—at least not just yet. No matter what list of risk factors were stacked against them (age, sex, race, alcohol abuse, depression, etc.), they were still enough committed to life to wait a bit and talk. They were, at least for the time being, willing to consider seeing how the rest of life might turn out.

As a risk to themselves, and in the language of ambivalence, they didn't so much want to die as to end their suffering and find a way to live. Therefore, getting a commitment to safety was relatively easy. To push our traveler's analogy here, they could agree to keep on living to see if the stretch of bumpy road they'd been traveling over was only a short section under construction on the way to a smooth interstate just ahead.

Where hope is easily restored by an interventionist or therapist, the risk of suicide diminishes rapidly. So rapidly, in fact, that without more than an occasional check to see if some subsequent problem re-triggers suicidal thoughts, you can pretty well forget the subject and, with the client, cross it off as a bum idea. Once life's problems begin to be solved—or even seem soluble—suicide quickly loses its appeal.

When Things Don't Go So Well

However, sometimes interventions don't go so well. Sometimes the person you're talking with is headed into what they see as the last mile of life. Sometimes the person isn't willing to give up suicide as a solution to either acute or life-long problems. Sometimes the person may be facing so many different problems all at once, it appears there is no way out. Having worked as hard as you can for an hour or more the sufferer remains—as if trapped in a Kafka play— unconvinced that hope can be revived. Simply put, the person doesn't believe you.

And why should someone believe you? You've only just met. For all the person knows, you're just some do-gooder who wouldn't know real psychological pain and suffering from a hole in the ground. And now here you are, after only just getting acquainted, asking him or her to give up the only solution that promised real relief.

As a rule, people who have invested a good deal of time, effort, and sometimes money into their suicide plan will not give it up without a struggle. They may not have figured out how to live successfully, but they *have* figured out how to die successfully.

Resistance To Help

For some people, coming up with a plan to suicide is the only real sense of personal control and success they've enjoyed lately. So if they feel you are closing in on them in an effort to get them to give up this plan, they may start to become resistant. Evasive maneuvers can include any of the following:

- They can't "remember" where they put the gun.
- They don't want to give up the stash of pills, just yet.
- Sure, they'll agree to see you the next day, but they're not making any promises.
- "Don't worry," they say, "I won't bother you when the time comes."
- "Thanks," they may say, "you've been real helpful. Until now I wasn't sure what to do. But I feel so much better after talking to you. Can I go now?"

When you start to get this kind of fogging job, you can figure it about two ways:

- These people don't trust you far enough to throw you (you're going to call the guys in the white coats, make them go to the hospital, remove them from their home, etc.)

or,

- You might be trustworthy, but it's still too soon to tell.

  Bottom line: You can't get a good faith commitment to safety and the future.

Suicide Risk Assessment

Now you have a tough call to make. You have to, in essence, decide whether what you do next is going to make the situation better or worse. I say "worse" because what you do next will probably run counter to the wishes of the suicidal person. But now that you've come this far, you too have no way out. If you've already decided the person you're talking to might need the safety and security of a psychiatric hospital (or something like it), you simply must move ahead. This "forcing the issue" will surely test the small alliance you've been working toward.

Putting someone into a psychiatric hospital is not always the best thing to do. But sometimes it is. This call, this judgment about what do with someone at risk who won't agree to be safe, is what mental health and other professionals (social workers, psychiatric nurses, counselors, psychologists, physicians, and psychiatrists) get paid to do. However well or poorly they do it, the reasons behind any such decision are based on the facts derived from a suicide risk assessment. And there are big problems with suicide risk assessment.

No matter how obvious a suicide seems to have been after the fact, the actual predicting of suicide is, essentially, impossible. There are inherent problems with predicting rare events, whether plane crashes, earthquakes, or the suicide of a given individual.

Yes, we know there will be plane crashes, but which plane and when? Yes, we know there will be earthquakes, but where and on what day? And, yes, many old, white, alcoholic males kill themselves, but precisely which ones, under what circumstances, and on which days?

Statistically speaking, no one dies of suicide. The United States base rate (12/100,000 per year) is simply too low. Your best bet, if you were to wager on who will die by suicide, is to bet that no given individual will. And you would win most such bets. Therefore, because of the absolute low base rates for suicide, all suicides are best predicted in reverse—as in, "I knew he was going to do it; all the signs were there."

Given the limitations of predicting the rare event, then, maybe the best thing we can to do is to learn some of the known risk factors, reduce these, let people know they are in high risk groups, and take all reasonable precautions to prevent suicide *once we know a person is feeling suicidal or thinking about taking his or her life.*

Note: While risk factors tend to be stable variables (age, race, psychiatric diagnosis, past attempts, divorced status, etc.), suicide actually occurs in a swirl of dynamic changes—changes over which we usually have little control. A statistically vulnerable person may be a low-risk suicide one week, but at high risk the next. (More of this under the risk management and therapy sections).

A Sample Of Risk Factors

So that you'll have some idea of the risk factors to be considered, here is partial list of the heavy hitters that, when added together, tend to increase the risk for suicide:

Age—Suicide increases with age.

Being male—More males commit suicide.

Ethnicity—More whites commit suicide than non-whites.

Depression—Acute or chronic.

Alcoholism—Any current or chronic use.

Prior psychiatric hospitalization—For any reason.

Physical illness—Recent diagnosis or declining health.

Divorced—Recent or remote.

Previous attempt—Recent or remote (recent is worse).

Family history of suicide—Especially a parent.

Threat of major loss—Financial, lover, job, etc.

Few (or no) social supports—Sudden isolation is worse.

Means available.

Plan and timetable in place.

Sense of being a burden to others.

Severe impulses to die.

History of poor coping.

Report of utter hopelessness.

This list could go on and on but, frankly, it is my opinion that relying solely on a rap sheet of risk factors to determine suicide risk is a dangerous practice. Likewise, relying too much on psychological test data, questionnaires, and inventories also leaves too many of the dynamic questions unanswered. No known test or interview schedule or cumulative sum of all the known risk factors to suicide will lead to a faultless prediction. Unfortunately, the hit rate for suicide based on the best of data remains discouragingly low—even among experienced clinicians. And clinical experience proves, again and again, just how wrong we can be.

Therefore, maybe the best thing to do is give up pretending any of us can be omniscient just now, go with what we've got, stay humble, and don't hold our opinions too strongly. We do, however, need to be able to answer the question, "How do we know what we know?" Because when it comes to pressuring a suicidal person into a more restricted environment, e.g., a psychiatric hospital, we have to have asked enough questions to form our opinion—however imperfect that opinion might prove to be.

The last thing to remember about risk assessment is that no matter what methods you use, how skillful you are, or how many times you have come to the same conclusion regarding similar suicidal people, your judgment will always be suspect. Just because you find an upset, jilted teenage girl at statistical low risk of taking her life when compared to an alcoholic, 60-year-old businessman who has a gun, bullets, and timetable to end his suffering, does not mean the girl will live and the man die. Just the opposite could happen. And, unfortunately, it sometimes does.

One Solution To The Risk Assessment Dilemma: The Good Faith Commitment

The only person who can really reduce the risk of suicide is the suicidal person. This sounds a little strange, but it is true. People bound and determined to kill themselves will often find a way—even tucked away in the relative security of a psychiatric unit while under a suicide watch. In a word, we need help from the suicidal person to ensure safety. And until the researchers come up with some sort of tried-and-true instruments to keep us all safe, our best bet is to continue to rely on the quality of the relationship we have with the suicidal person and the power of treatment in safe environments.

The Decision To Hospitalize

If you think about the suicidal person's journey toward self-destruction as a process with a beginning, a middle, and an end, then you can see that by the time such a person is *unwilling* to make a commitment to safety he or she is, by reason of resistance and probable emotional condition, well down the road to death and unable to see a way clear to turn around or let anybody else do the driving. Such a person is no longer safe and, in the language of the law, now presents a "danger to self."

Basically, if you cannot get a good faith commitment to safety you have no choice but to hospitalize, or at least get people involved who can help you make this decision. If a given person feels out of control, or you judge that person to be out of control and unable to give a firm and considered commitment to stay safe (due to alcohol or drug intoxication, an active psychosis, too many uncontrollable players and possibilities, etc.), then hospitalization is probably indicated.

Unless you are one, it is not your job to second guess mental health professionals as to whether an admission to a hospital is indicated. If in doubt (and especially if you can't get a second opinion on your assessment), plan to step outside of the intervention relationship and get some serious help. What you don't want is to steer someone away from the hospital who should have gone, or to give in to the person's anger now that you've confronted him or her.

Failing the suicidal person's willingness and/or ability to make a commitment to safety, and to give up the means of suicide and otherwise cooperate in his or her own future and well being, we're left with only two questions:

• Are we going to the hospital the easy way (voluntarily)?

or,

• Are we going to the hospital the hard way (involuntarily)?

Note: Once you have made up your mind that the suicidal person you're working with is not safe and needs a supervised and safe environment, *don't be talked out of it.*

So you'll be prepared for this confrontation, here are some typical things suicidal people say to avoid going to the hospital:

- "But I'll be all right. Honest I will!"
- "I was only kidding. I'm not going to kill myself."
- "Gee, why are you taking all this so seriously?"
- "Mental hospital? Do I look crazy to you? Of course I'm not going to any hospital."
- "Hospital!? I can't to go to a hospital. Who will look after my cat?"
- "I'm already broke. I can't afford to go to a hospital."

Standing Firm

Having made up your mind to ensure safety, expect some anger from the suicidal person. After all, you're restricting—or threatening to restrict—this person's freedom. Some may get downright nasty. Others will call you names. Still others may threaten to sue. These reactions are unfortunate, but unavoidable. Because if, down deep, you believe this person is still at risk and is only now struggling to break free from the safety net you are constructing, you simply cannot back away from your decision to get more help, including ensuring a hospitalization.

In fact, to back off your decision at this juncture may amount to a tacit agreement that you've changed your mind about how hopeful the future really is. The suicidal person, therefore, may interpret your reversal as, "Ha! I was right...there is no hope."

Strong Feelings

At this point in any difficult suicide assessment interview, strong feelings are evident. The suicidal person came in upset and may now be more upset because of being confronted with the inability to manage his or her own life. Autonomy jeopardized, he or she may claim his or her constitutional rights are being infringed and argue that this is still a free country and that you can't force your will on the person. This can be very genuine hostility, and unless you are from some other solar system, you too will be feeling some strong emotions.

The good feelings of empathy and understanding you felt toward the suicidal person only moments before may be replaced with boredom, anger (fear), or frustration.

Boredom. Watch out for boredom! Feeling suddenly bored with a suicidal person's problems may signal that you are, emotionally, withdrawing from the relationship at a high rate of speed. After all the time you've just spent together, now the person doesn't want to play ball. You're tired, it's late and, after all, there are better things to do than keep spinning your wheels with someone who can't seem to make a decision.

Anger. As fear is usually behind anger, expect at least the possibility that you will begin to feel a bit of anger. In this case (where you're trying to save a life), the fear comes from the feeling that you're failing. Here you've been trying like hell to save this person's life and, after giving it your best shot, you're now being told to butt out. Becoming angry is an extremely common emotional reaction to someone who has placed his or her life in your hands and now wants to tie those hands behind your back.

Frustration. Unless you do suicide assessments for a living, expect to feel at least frustrated. A lot is at stake. The person is now less than cooperative and also playing hardball. Without necessarily meaning to, the person will test you, try you, and push you to the limits of your kindness. It's okay, though—a lot of people have been letting this person down lately. You just happen to be, maybe, the last one in line.

Handling Your Emotions

Feeling boredom, anger (fear), and frustration—and knowing these are normal and on schedule—may help you identify them as they occur. Owning such emotions is good, not bad. It means you're on target and know what's going on inside you. Depending on circumstances, it may be quite appropriate to say to the suicidal person,

"You know, I'm getting a little scared here. Despite our having talked together and having gotten started on understanding some of your problems, you're acting like you don't want me to help you any more. Have you had this experience with others?"

You may get a helpful answer here and one that can put the relationship right again. Very often the suicidal person will come in with a history of similar unhelpful conversations. Your question may cut right to the heart of the matter by acknowledging everyone's sense of impotence and helplessness.

Another congruent statement to make is,

"I realize you may not be able to make a commitment to safety right now. That may be okay for you, but it isn't okay for me. And I'm here to do the best job I can to keep you alive."

By showing the suicidal person you're willing to make a stand, he or she will generally calm down and go along with the program. Based on your objectivity and good judgment, you've decided to pry the person's fingers from the wheel and take over the driving. As the designated driver (the sane and sober one), you did the right thing. Later, and this proves true more often than not, the suicidal person will return and thank you for having the courage to act in his or her best interest.

Voluntary Hospitalization

If a suicidal person unwilling to commit to safety can, however reluctantly, be convinced to enter a hospital voluntarily, this is best. Involuntary hospitalization can get ugly and is always tougher on the patient's sense of pride and self worth.

Voluntary hospitalization is relatively easy to arrange, provided you've done a little homework and have listed the essential resource information you'll need on the back leaf of this book. Your main message to the suicidal person is that you want him or her to be safe. You want the person to get a good night's rest, talk with some doctors and nurses, and otherwise put things on hold for a while. Suicidal people have been trying like the dickens to solve some damn problem or other and, very often, will finally welcome the chance for a little relief—even after a show of initial resistance. Later, they can explain to their friends, "I didn't want to, but they insisted."

Preparing the Way

Knowing a little about the nature of modern psychiatric hospitalization and sharing this information with the suicidal person may ease the transition to a safe environment. Addressing these fears (imagined or real) is the best, quickest, and most effective way to get someone at risk to agree to go voluntarily. Here are a few facts to help you in your efforts:

• Hospital stays these days are short; from a few days to a couple of weeks.

• The staff are well trained and know about the pain and suffering suicidal people experience.

• As a voluntary patient, you don't *have* to do everything they ask you to do—including taking medications.

• Shock treatments are largely of historical interest only and can never be given without patient permission.

• You have all sorts of patient rights (these vary from state to state, but usually include access to a phone, visitors, religious practice, confidentiality, and so forth).

• Modern psychiatric hospitals are places of healing that respect the dignity of the person; they are not snake pits or prisons.

Here, then, are the usual and customary steps to a psychiatric hospitalization:

1) Call the psychiatrist (or, in some cases an emergency room physician) who's agreed to hospitalize your client. He or she will need the following info:

   • Age; sex; nature of crisis; presence of alcohol, drugs, and what (if any) medications the person is on. Provide the phone number of a family member or significant other.

• Some doctors will want more information, but unless you're a highly trained professional, they shouldn't expect the world. Some may want to know who's paying the bill.

2) To knock down worries and anticipate the usual excuses of why going to the hospital is inconvenient just now, agree to make arrangements for baby sitting, pets, jobs, apartment managers, or whatever else stands between the person and his or her safety.

3) If not available by a responsible adult, arrange transportation. Most suicidal people can get themselves to the hospital, but why take chances? Just about any responsible adult can get someone to the hospital. Cabbies do fine. If the person is acutely suicidal and wants to die *right now*, do not put any non-professional in the job of saving a life; instead call 911.

4) With youth, have a parent or responsible person available at the time of admission to give both support and reassurance.

5) For your own sake (and so you'll get a good night's sleep), have the hospital call you when your referral is safely tucked in bed.

Exception: If you have reason to believe the person you're dealing with has taken an overdose or may be bleeding, call a paramedic unit (also on the back flap). Folks who overdose often haven't a clue about how much of what kind of medication or poison or combination thereof they have taken. Unless you are properly trained to assess such medical emergencies, let the folks who know take over.

Involuntary Hospitalization

Involuntary hospitalization is a last resort. It is what we are obliged to do when someone we have identified as at imminent risk of suicide refuses to cooperate in his or her own welfare. If we cannot get a good faith commitment to a safe outpatient program or a voluntary hospitalization, then we have no choice but to follow the law.

Involuntary commitment laws vary from state to state, but all of them basically address the following question: By reason of a mental illness, does this person represent a threat to the safety and welfare of himself or others?

If the answer to this question is yes—by reason of facts established in the petition of clinical findings and based upon the opinion of attending professionals—then the court may commit the person to the care and safety of the facility, usually for no more than two weeks. These facilities are usually state-approved psychiatric hospitals or units within general medical hospitals, or state mental hospitals.

Unless you are in some official capacity and have the appropriate legal protection and capacity to cause a suicidal person to enter a psychiatric hospital involuntarily, you don't need to know or even understand all the particulars of the involuntary treatment laws operative in your state. But you do need to know how to access the people responsible for carrying out these laws and when to call them.

The Involuntary Treatment System

Each state and county may have a little different system. For your own sake (and for the sake of any suicidal person with whom you may come into contact), take a little time and learn how your system works. Then put the names and numbers of the appropriate contacts on the back flap of this book. When you can answer the following questions, consider yourself properly schooled:

- Who is responsible to evaluate suicidal persons for possible involuntary detention where you live? Sheriff? Police? Mental health center? If these folks do not coordinate (among themselves), who should you call first?

- Do the people who conduct these evaluations make home visits? Will they come to your place of work? If not, how do you get the suicidal person to them?

- How long may a person be detained before being evaluated for involuntary commitment to treatment?

- How long can any involuntary commitment last?

- Can a patient become voluntary once committed?

- Will you have to testify against the person you are trying to help in order to secure a detention? A commitment?

- At what age may a youth be detained against his or her will in a treatment facility?

- What information will you need to have in hand when you call whoever it is you must call?

If you can answer this handful of questions, you should be in good shape if and when you have to pull the string and bring in the power of the law to stop a suicide. If you can't answer these questions, call your local mental health agency and get the answers.

Note: A few crisis treatment systems will provide on-site evaluation and intervention, referral services, respite services, and a complete community safety net instead of a forced hospitalization. The good news is, these same people should and will take responsibility for the survival plan and its implementation.

The general rule to invoking an involuntary hospitalization is that it is not up to just us (mental health professionals, school counselors, therapists, nurses, or any human service worker caught up in a suicide assessment situation) to make the final decision about the ultimate safety of a given individual. This is, rather, the court's decision. Therefore, rather than second guess the complicated social, psychological, and legal process that can lead to an infringement of constitutional rights for the sake of safety, let the courts decide.

The Burden To Save A Life

Anytime you get involved in the decisions about a suicidal person's future, you have just accepted one of life's greatest burdens: to see to it someone doesn't die. Personally, I cannot think of a heavier burden. Even doctors doing very risky brain surgery have a room full of people to back them up, offer consolation if things don't turn out, and stand up for them in court later (if need be) to swear, "Yes, Dr. Smith did everything humanly possible."

We who work with suicidal people should be so lucky. On the upside, however, where else could you find a greater and more potentially rewarding challenge?

Staying In Psychological Shape So You Stay Useful

Those of us who work with suicidal people must take care of ourselves. As suicide interventionists and therapists, we're no good to anyone unless we're in reasonably good spirits, getting enough rest and still active in the field of human services. As there is nothing like a student, client, or patient completing a suicide to severely damage our own self-esteem and threaten our ability to work successfully with others, it is therefore essential that we, too, are reasonably protected from this potential trauma.

One way to protect ourselves is *to make every reasonable effort to be sure our charge was safe and our duty carried out so that we are personally as safe from the traumatic effects of a suicide attempt or completion as we can be.*

All any of us can do in this work is our best. Fortunately, our best is usually quite enough. As I once remarked to a staff person many years ago after a tough suicide consult, "If this work wasn't noble, I wouldn't do it." And I remind myself of this statement frequently.

3 ⋯

Treatment, Management, and Therapy

From the title of this chapter and the direction the rest of this book will take, it may appear I am making an assumption that all suicidal people suffer from one or another form of mental or emotional disorder. I am not making this assumption. However, because we know so little about those apparently mentally healthy people who end their lives by suicide, I must stick to what I know.

More, both clinical experience and available research strongly suggest that most of those who attempt or complete a suicide are suffering from some sort of emotional, drug or alcohol, or major relationship conflict. Some are in treatment for these problems; most are not. If you look at life over its entire cycle and examine your own worst crises, developmental phases, tragedies, losses, and the symptoms that accompanied these stressful episodes, you will quickly understand the old joke that says, "The main difference between the emotionally disturbed and the rest of us is that the rest of us haven't been diagnosed yet." Therefore, I will for now, and for the purposes of this book, assume there is no clear line between those of us who are not suicidal today and those who are.

As used in this book, each of these terms (treatment, management, and therapy) has a little different meaning. The management of suicidal patients is not the same thing as the treatment of the disorders out of which suicidal thinking and behavior arise. Treatment may include medications, socialization programs, case management, and the like, whereas therapy—as I prefer to use the term—is how we use ourselves, our brains, and our hearts to help others heal. In this section I will briefly address management and treatment in order to set the backdrop for the therapy of suicidal patients, the section which follows.

Good management creates a safe environment, ensures sound procedures for the delivery of appropriate treatments, and lowers the risk that a patient will die by suicide—both during and after treatment is delivered. However, the cold, merciless Nurse Ratched in Ken Kesey's *One Flew Over the Cuckoo's Nest* is a good manager. She is also quite able to deliver appropriate medications on schedule (good treatment). But Nurse Ratched is not (and I think I met her once) a good therapist. To ensure the best outcome for suicidal patients, we need not only good management of good treatment, but good therapy as well.

Good Treatment

There are, fundamentally, three categories of people suffering from mental and emotional illness at high risk for suicide. Each category presents a different challenge, both in terms of management and therapy. They can be divided, roughly, as follows:

1) *Depressions, panic disorders, and relationship conflicts complicated by anger and/or mixed emotional*

reactions. Secondary personality disorders may occur in any of these categories as well.

These problems are, generally, both time-limited and highly treatable. The majority of people who become suicidal as a result of such temporary episodes of distress are never diagnosed or treated, despite the availability of good and effective treatments. Early education, diagnosis, and referral would seem to be the keys to saving lives among this large number of people.

Depression is extremely common throughout the age range. As depression is possibly the best understood of all the emotional illnesses, the diagnosis is simple and the treatment is straightforward. (See Special Topics Section for more details on depression, its diagnosis, and its treatment.) Likewise, relationship conflicts are increasingly better understood and, generally, yield to a variety of individual, couples, and group counseling approaches.

As many youths fall into the combined category of depression complicated by relationship conflicts, if they are still living with their parents, family therapy is generally the treatment of choice. Having worked with many school counselors whose job descriptions and work settings do not permit the kind of frontal assault on seriously dysfunctional families suicidal youths often require, I have found that many times the best thing to do is to triage and refer outside of the educational system.

2) *Chronic mental illness.* Persons with serious, long-term chronic mental illness are at high, lifetime risk for suicide. These disorders would include schizophrenia,

organic mental disorders, bi-polar illness, recurrent major depressive episodes, and any number of the severe and persistent personality disorders. People with two or more diagnoses (the dually diagnosed) seem especially at risk— particularly when the second diagnosis is alcoholism or drug addiction.

Good treatment for those with chronic mental illness includes: careful diagnosis; appropriate physical, neurological, and psychological workups; consideration of psychotropic medications; and—at the very least—long-term, community-based case management services.

In my own view, community mental health centers offer the best available treatment to the chronically mentally ill—partly because it is their primary business, but also because they will often have day treatment services, a psycho-social rehabilitation club or program, and the backing of families and advocates for the mentally ill. In terms of range of service, a mental health center should have psychiatric coverage, case management services, counseling services, and access to a comprehensive emergency response system. For the seriously and chronically mentally ill at risk of suicide, nothing beats the quality of care offered by a quality community mental health center.

3) *Alcoholism and Drug Abuse.* As a group of patients, alcoholics and addicts represent the third group who remain at high suicide risk—not only while they use, but also when they stop using.

Good treatment for this large, complex, suicide-vulnerable group of people is, in my view, still hard to find. True, there are many fine inpatient programs, but these work only for some, are time-limited, and may or may not have a good follow-up program. If high priced, availability can be a problem. Also, only a very few such programs are sensitive to the special needs of the elderly.

In the outpatient mode, and regardless of formal degree, too few private practitioners have had adequate training in the diagnosis and treatment of addictions. Unaware of the degree of drinking or drug use in their patients, they unwittingly enable chemical abuse by failing to confront it adequately and, in so doing, may inadvertently increase—not lower—the risk of suicide.

Federal and state drug and alcohol programs tend to be under-funded and excessively rigid. Worse, because substance abuse staff are inadequately trained in the diagnosis of co-existing mental and emotional disorders and the concurrent presence of self-destructive thinking in their recovering patients, they often become immobilized when a patient says he or she is suicidal. Too often, when confronted by a suicidal patient, they think "refer," not "Now, how do I help Charlie through this?"

The point is this: Once a problem with drugs or alcohol has been found, treatment for sobriety is *always* indicated. And once a drug or alcohol abuser has been found to be suicidal, treatment for suicidality is also indicated. Treating both at once is, in my view, the preferred approach—especially since intoxication affects brain function, decreases inhibitory controls, impairs judgment and, therefore, greatly increases the risk of suicide.

Finally, my reason for outlining the fundamentals of good treatment for these three known groups at risk of suicide is this: *There is no substitute for good treatment.* Public education won't do it. Talk therapies by themselves won't do it. Self-help books and self-help groups won't do it. Until we can get the people in trouble good treatment (through public awareness raising, making services readily available, and by aggressive outreach programs to high-risk groups who do not self-refer), we cannot, in my view, expect to substantially reduce the base rate of suicide in our communities.

Good Management (Inpatient)

Like the old saw that the worst thing you can do if you're sick is go to a doctor, many suicides occur *in* psychiatric hospitals. Therefore, in considering the patient's safety, it is well to remember that no one, no facility, and no hospital can guarantee it—which is why the interpersonal context and the patient's good-faith commitment to safety is so important.

In my own view, psychiatric hospitalization is a last resort. Unless you work in them, inpatient units can be frightening places, and while the reason to hospitalize is to both increase the patient's safety and begin treatment, the fact remains that being admitted to a "mental institution" seldom improves your reputation or self-esteem.

For many patients (and especially the mildly depressed and the personality disordered), I'm not even sure there is good evidence that hospitalization for suicidality alone doesn't do as much harm as it does good—especially when you consider the problems that seemed worth dying for are still there to be solved on the day of discharge. For working people with limited financial resources, ten days in the hospital may remove them not only from the support of their family and friends, but can also leave them with a staggering hospital bill.

Still, if the decision to hospitalize has been made for the usual safety reasons (remove the patient from a suicidogenic situation, reduce acute tension and panic, get away from drugs and alcohol, can't get a No-Suicide Contract, etc.), at least you will have some assurance that, compared to the situation from which you are extricating the person, things probably won't get any worse. And, when you are handed a hot suicide crisis, "things not getting worse" is a perfectly acceptable outcome.

One way to think about a hospitalization is that it is a way to *buy time* for the suicidal person—time to think things over, allow a crisis to cool down, and to share his or her predicament with others so that the healing can begin. Hospitals are, by the way, the best places to get the necessary medical and psychiatric workups, try out needed medications, and make plans for more definitive outpatient treatment.

Each psychiatric hospital, residential treatment center, nursing home, structured group home, or any facility where people spend the night is generally considered an "inpatient" setting—at least in terms of the increased responsibility that attends what staff do or don't do once they know a resident presents some clear and present danger to him- or herself. While I strongly advise any such unit to carefully review the current laws in their states and consult with an attorney experienced in this area of risk management, here are a few of the obvious obligations once someone (anyone) on your staff has identified a suicidal patient:

1) Arrange a consultation with in-house psychiatrists, suicide consultants, senior staff, or others who can, in essence, provide a second (and back-up) opinion as to what steps should be taken to keep the patient safe.

2) Determine if the patient is safe within the present ward, room, or facility. If determined safe, chart this decision and any planned action.

3) If the patient is determined unsafe to be alone, implement a suicide watch, usually defined as checking the patient visually at least every 5, 10, 15, or 30 minutes. Consideration of placement in a restricted environment (locked ward, different facility, etc.) is also indicated. Most hospitals have several levels of special precautions for suicidal patients. The so-called "one-on-one" level is the highest and is one in which, essentially, the patient is under constant surveillance.

   Generally speaking, all such calls for intense patient supervision are made by the physician in charge and involve a balancing of advantages and disadvantages. A psychologically competent patient is much more easily managed in such circumstances than, say, a rapidly-cycling, psychotic, manic-depressive patient whose plunge into a suicidal crisis can, literally, occur at any moment. In some cases, suicide precautions can become a deadly game to be played and, if won by the patient, can have disastrous effects on staff and hospital.

4) If medications are to be dispensed, dispense them in non-lethal doses.

5) Remove all means of suicide. This is, as experienced hospital staff know, extremely difficult to do.

6) Once suicide risk has been determined, such determination needs to be transmitted to those who need to know: staff on other shifts, doctors, the charge nurse, and, possibly, family members and the outpatient therapist. Collaboration is key.

Outpatient Management

Often, the first decision faced by an outpatient therapist is: Should this patient be in the hospital? If not now, then when? And under what circumstances?

This is a very complicated decision and, as indicated in the sections on assessment, is best dealt with early on as part of the initial and ongoing intervention(s) and therapy. As a psychiatric hospitalization, in and of itself, can create a crisis and enhance the patient's desire to die, this is the very best time to make team decisions.

When considering the various factors that weigh into a decision to keep the patient out of the hospital, it may help to understand that in the sometimes long haul of therapy for suicidal people, no single episode of psychiatric inpatient treatment is going to "fix" what's wrong.

Likewise, no single hospitalization is going to prevent the recurrence of a cyclical depression, or the tragedy of some unanticipated loss, or the recurrence of episodic drinking that leads to relationship conflict, or the ordinary and progressive downward spiral of health and happiness that accompanies addictive disorders. Where hospital stays are short, the problems of the suicide-vulnerable are long. The race to healing will be won by the tortoise, not the hare, by the outpatient therapist, not the inpatient nurse.

A Safety Net

Good outpatient management means installing a community safety net while ensuring good treatment and therapy. If we begin with the premise that the hospital is neither a necessary, particularly safe, nor even helpful place to put people who are in the medium to lower risk ranges of taking their own lives, what, then, comprises a good community safety net?

The fundamentals include the following:

- A network of people who know the status of the suicidal person and can act on his or her behalf to ensure some modicum of safety.

- A pre-planned access route to hospitalization if the need arises.

- An agreed-to, mutually understood plan of action should an unforeseen crisis arise. This plan would be known by all involved.

- The flexibility to increase the frequency of appointments, family sessions, and conjoint sessions with spouses or significant others as the need arises. (I often instruct staff to keep a couple hours open in their schedule at the end of the week so they can meet crises head-on and in a timely fashion.)

- A backup therapist readily available to the patient when you are away, out of town, or otherwise not available. A crisis number, an on-call number, whatever... there must be a short, open bridge between you and the patient.

- A close working relationship with the primary care doctor or any others involved in the patient's treatment and therapy. Sometimes a suicidal patient will signal suicidal feelings to only one person in the network. Assuming everyone else in the network has gotten the same message (and is taking care of business) is a terrible and often preventable mistake.

- A method to ensure medication compliance. Many suicidal patients store up meds with the intention of overdosing if things don't get better. As medications cannot work if they stay in the bottle, check and double check to ensure prescribed meds are being taken *as prescribed*. Failure to confirm this medication compliance can sometimes be interpreted by the patient as a coded message to "go ahead and kill yourself."

- The assurance of as safe a community environment as you can get. With the patient's permission, involve anyone who can help. Parents, a brother, a cousin, anyone who the patient feels can share a bit of the pain. In some locales, there are even trained crisis respite workers who will, under the supervision and direction of mental health professionals, spend anywhere from a few hours to a few days with a patient in an acute suicidal crisis—thus providing an alternative to a questionable hospitalization.

- The assurance that case assignment and professional responsibility is clear, not only to others on your staff, but especially to the patient and his or her family. Suicidal people who have contact with an agency or group of helpers, or even a single practitioner, are not helped when left with the distinct feeling they've just been suspended in what I call a mid-air referral, e.g., "Someone will get back to you by Monday." While there may be some relief from calling Dial-a-Prayer, suicidal people need a sense of having connected with someone down here on the planet surface. Fail to make them feel this connection, and all the other work can go for nothing.

Clearly, this list of outpatient management strategies is far from complete. So please feel free to improvise and invent anything and everything you can to create a network of support to help keep the suicidal patient safe until things can be turned around.

4 _____ ...

A Note To Therapists

Despite the value of such miracles as antipsychotic and antidepressant medications, the best therapy for people who have talked themselves into suicide is to talk them back out again. But before we can do this well, we need to know something about ourselves. Therefore, allow me to share a few of my biases.

Healers Matter Most

It is my strong belief that the treatment of suicidal people is fundamentally the treatment of hopelessness. Hopelessness (and I've defined it at some length in the Special Topics section), is basically a psychological state in which the sufferer believes nothing positive will ever happen again. However arrived at, this overwhelming affective and cognitive state is, in my view, contagious. And I mean for healers.

For example, if you've ever worked with someone seriously suicidal who has just spent an hour giving you chapter and verse as to why life is no longer worth living, then you already know that therapists are not immune to the contagion of hopelessness. After a really despairing and stressful hour with someone hell-bent on self-destruction, you may find yourself thinking, "Gee... this person really needs professional help."

This sudden feeling of impotence, ineffectiveness, helplessness, and generalized professional enfeeblement brought on by interacting with suicidal patients suggests (to me at least) that none of us is immune from the hopelessness virus. Therefore, part of my mission here will be to try to inoculate you against the frightening specter of coming to believe, as your client does, that life isn't worth living after all. Because as soon as you become as pessimistic and hopeless about your patient's prospects as he or she is, you become part of the problem, not part of the solution.

Even though helping people doesn't get any tougher than working with folks who want to die, we can do it, and we can do it well. The data are in: Therapy works! So, to keep us all buoyant and optimistic about this business of saving lives, here are my thoughts on those therapist variables we all need to consider and keep in mind.

• However we're trained, we should be comfortable with the subject of suicide and its inherent potential for violence and death. Some therapists take a chill when a patient mentions suicide. Others feel a stab of anxiety. This is okay. But if you freeze, panic, and/or otherwise become immobilized by suicide talk, either work your way through it or don't offer to treat suicidal people. What suicidal people don't need is a therapist who has seized up.

   Note: If you must panic, at least panic later when the patient isn't looking. I have always found rounding up a colleague or two very helpful when I need to panic.

• We must see a fundamental human being in the suicidal sufferer—not some strange or bizarre person who is unknowable. To do this, it helps to see ourselves as ordinary, not extraordinary. We can never go wrong if our patients see us as understanding, genuine, and warm. Plain old garden-variety compassion will save more suicidal sufferers than all the technical skills in the world.

For what it's worth, it has always helped me to think of life as a bowl of soup; existentially, we're all in it together. The suicidal person next to us is, by comparison, only in a little deeper.

• Regarding formal education, it helps to know how suicidal people think, how they got into this particular pickle, and what can be done to keep them safe while they get better. This does not require a Ph.D. Far from it. We need some facts, some general resource information and, together with understanding the fundamentals of crisis intervention and how to employ a few therapy skills, most anyone who is just a little smarter than the average bear should qualify for this work.

Once the therapist learns to tolerate tears, childish acting out, expressions of deeply-felt grief and rage, and veiled threats to suicide (and how not to panic when the patient does), the rest of this work is a piece of cake. Human suffering is generic; learning to see it, share it, accept it, and let it be until things get better is what mostly this healing business is all about.

• We all need a supportive work environment. We need to be respected for this work. Even honored. After all, saving lives is a serious undertaking. To feel good about ourselves, we need not only a good professional back-up system, we need to like the people we work with, and they need to like us. Where morale is low and poor communication exists among members of a treatment team, all suicidal patients are at increased risk.

- We, ourselves, should not be suicidal. Since objectivity cannot be maintained when our problems too closely mirror those of our patients, we should never offer to treat someone suicidal when we are contemplating our own death. Seriously problematic on the face of it, offering to help others under such circumstances is, in the view of many, unethical.

  If you've been thinking about suicide yourself—which is hardly extraordinary among therapists—take yourself off any case in which suicide is an issue and get some help. Likewise, if for some reason you happen to believe that suicide is fated (e.g., those who try it once will eventually die by suicide), get out of this work. No friend to either therapist or patient, fatalistic thinking is a killer.

  Having worked with several suicidal therapists down through the years, I reiterate this finding of fact: With the manpower crisis in mental health, we can't afford to lose a single one of us. On the other hand, neither can we afford to lose a single patient because a therapist, case manager, psychologist, nurse, or physician has not yet dealt successfully with his or her own suicide potential.

  However, if you have been suicidal in the past, worked through it and are now, as Ernest Hemingway once said, "stronger in the broken places," this could be a big plus in the empathy department.

- If you are the survivor of a suicide yourself (parent, brother, sister, lover, husband, wife, child, etc.), please talk this over with a therapist. Sharing this tragedy with a colleague or a suicide survivor group can help, but the objectivity and nature of a professional therapy arrangement may be best if you're going to do this work for a living. To work with suicidal people, we need to take special care to heal ourselves first.

> *Note:* In my limited experience with counselors who have not dealt therapeutically with the suicide of, say, a parent, their reactions to suicidal clients are rarely within normal limits. Often such therapists become submarine drivers and slip beneath the waves of denial. "Nothing going on here," they say to themselves and others. This denial always represents some risk to the suicidal sufferer. How much risk, I haven't a clue.

• Last, it is my strong view that humor helps us do this work. Not the kind of humor taken at the patient's expense, but humor anchored in compassion. Humor gives us all a sudden, sure distance from the source of our pain. It allows us to think the unthinkable and to find solace in the fact that, after all, none of us is getting out of here alive.

More, empathic humor is, at least in my clinical experience, absolutely incompatible with killing yourself. Once, while interviewing a hospitalized alcoholic logger who had, in a drunken suicidal rage, driven his logging truck off a cliff, I asked how was it possible he didn't die. He said, "Well, I was so drunk I picked the wrong cliff. It was only two feet high." Then he laughed. "If I'd have been sober, I'd have found a much higher cliff. And now *you* want *me* to quit drinkin'!?"

We both laughed. Wit, as someone once said, is the only thing between us and the dark.

5 _____ •••

The Therapy of Hope

Before I pass along the specific tools I use to help suicidal people in the counseling session, you need to know that, even as a graduate student, I was something of a maverick. Try as I might, I never found a "school of therapy" in which to place my total faith. The worst kind of eclectic, I liked everything from the behavioral methods of B.F. Skinner to the spooky meandering of Carl Jung to the practicalities of Albert Ellis and the caring tone of Carl Rogers. As I had excellent clinical supervisors in all these schools, I became, as it were, a fatherless child.

If pressed today, I would only confess to being something of a cognitive-behaviorist, but one with strong existential tendencies who, if pushed to the wall, would admit to an abiding affection for traditional dynamic theory. I would also admit that late at night, when no one's around, I read sociobiology and toy with the strong possibility that evolutionary theory has been given too little attention in the whole field of human understanding.

Weak on theory, I've tried to make up for this deficit with techniques—some of which seem to work pretty well. As a student I was always disappointed my professors couldn't seem to tell me exactly what I should do or say in a session to help people. Sometimes I wondered if they even themselves. For whatever they might be worth, here are 30 suggestions, techniques, and strategies for working directly with suicidal people.

The Frame

In general, my approach to working with most suicidal people is to challenge, directly, the patient's *thinking*. This must be done in a caring context, but the fundamental work is confrontational in nature. Using a cognitive therapy approach, the work is active, structured, focused on attitudes, beliefs, and especially, the patient's interpretations of reality. The sufferer's beliefs are viewed as hypotheses, *not* realities. As such, they are also not "givens." Just because someone has concluded a situation is hopeless doesn't mean it is hopeless at all—*it only means that person **thinks** it is hopeless.*

The goal of this therapeutic approach is to bring about nothing less than the way a patient perceives and understands life's problems. Unless the patient sees old problems differently, and with more clarity, and in less polarized terms, no new solutions can be found. Research on problem solving has repeatedly shown that, when we are frustrated by some familiar problem, we don't reach for new solutions, we just get a bigger hammer.

Therefore, we must help suicidal people understand how they are thinking (generally, not well), how the world "seems" to them, and how, if they may make errors in logic based on misinterpreted or misread "facts," these errors can lead to wrong formulations and wrong actions. Any failure on our part to address these cognitive glitches and the impaired logic most suicidal people fall heir to as they trudge around and around in the deepening rut of depression and hopelessness can leave them with the same lousy conclusion: I must die.

The talking part of this therapy is head-on and sometimes quite directive. With acutely suicidal people, I am purposely not passive. To be so runs the risk that the patient may conclude we are not about urgent business. Make no mistake: *We are about urgent business.* Generally, we don't have all day to wonder about how things might turn out. So, both physically and psychologically, I lean forward into the relationship, actively ask questions and, if the process needs a leader early on, I've no reluctance whatever to take on the job.

But however directive I may be in the beginning, the work is always within the context of a caring, therapeutic alliance. Relationship is everything. The strongest wall between a suicidal person and the hopelessness that kills is the one built by relationships. Therapeutic interventions, techniques, and strategies are fine, but they are all nothing compared to a genuine, right-on understanding between a therapist and a patient that, no matter what, they are in this together.

A Dash Of Theory

Although suicide may be the most poorly understood form of human behavior and is almost always both complex and multi-determined, a great deal of therapy time can be saved by understanding that, in many cases, the suicidal person has been, or is about to be, abandoned. Suicide, like a tango, usually takes two.

From attachment theory we know that people who fail to bond with their parental figures are at high risk. Likewise, people whose early bonds with nuturing others were broken are also at increased risk. Therefore, to quickly grasp the most frequent dynamic underlying a suicidal crisis, ask, "Who in your life will be most affected by your death?"

The answer to this question will never be less than rich in dynamic, clinical information. Most often, it will tell you who in the suicidal person's life is threatening to leave, change, or otherwise shatter a fundamental bond. Where this bond has been shattered before, the risk of suicide is much enhanced.

When the bonds that bind us one with another are threatened, we become both frightened and furious. Yet, because we cannot hurt the one we love and need so desperately, we cannot show this fury. Question: Where does this fury go? Many theorists argue this fury turns in upon the self—which is why suicide is often called "murder in the 180th degree."

However useful the following suggestions and techniques may be in the restoration of hope, and if this abandonment dynamic is at work, teaching the suicidal person a bit about attachment theory, and the nature of human needs, can prove extremely helpful. By explaining what happens when this need for others is frustrated (anger, rage, guilt, and grief), and showing the suicidal person just where these feelings are coming from by walking (talking) them through the exact events that precipitated the crisis in the first place, you can often bring about a rapid reversal in suicidal ideation and a lowering of imminent risk. This, however, is not the end of therapy; rather, it is but a good beginning.

Building The Therapeutic Relationship

Putting together a working therapy alliance is easy. Most of the work has already been done for you. Most anywhere you might see a suicidal person you will have a quiet office, no interruptions, the gift of confidentiality and, except for recent immigrants to America, a more or less clear and shared cultural understanding that this helping relationship is something special, extraordinary, and probably time-limited. If therapy goes well, you will also have a beginning, a middle, and an end. So long as you are a reasonably nice person and nobody's fool, all you have to do is take heed of the following suggestions:

•   Make it plain from the very start that you're on the patient's side. Most suicidal people feel no one is on their "side." In some cases, no one has ever been on their side. So put yourself there. You can even say, "I'm on your side."

    If a hug is appropriate at the end of the first session, a hug from the side and around the shoulder says in the most powerful terms possible, "Hey, look, I'm on your side."

•   To make sure the patient feels respected and truly cared for, arrange your interview space so there are no obstacles between you. A big desk between you says, "Don't get too close." Suicidal people need to know "close" is possible.

•   Because interruptions break moods, stop necessary tears, and do not respect the importance of the communication between the healer and the sufferer, allow no phone calls, people walking into your space, or other such nonsense.

- If you can, let the patient set the personal space between you. Saying, "Please sit where you like" takes care of this. For folks who feel they have no control of anything, even deciding where they'd like to sit can be helpful.

- Same goes for the name. Talking about something as important as names helps break the ice and cuts through a lot of unnecessary formalities that can slow building the alliance. Ask, "How would you like me to call you?" Some people may say, "Mr. Cratchit." Others say, "Fred." Fred is generally better. And clear up right away how you'd like to be called. Sometimes an early, first-name familiarity helps, and sometimes it doesn't. This is your call.

- Talk openly about the issue of trust. Ask, "Has anyone in the past tried to help you?" If the answer is yes, find out if the help was helpful. If it wasn't (the counselor failed the patient in some way, violated a boundary, broke a confidence, etc.), trust will come slowly.

  Likewise, if the person has never received any thoughtful, compassionate help from another human being, trust has *always* been an issue. Given this history, building trust may take even more time. Weeks, even months may pass before a deep trust-bond is formed. Don't get discouraged; the race to healing is not won by the swift, but by those who endure.

  If the person has been in a healing, trusting relationship at one time, build on this, learn about it, honor it, and keep it in mind as a counterweight to the person's current sense of abandonment.

- Never finish a first session without learning something positive about the person's life: some past victory, an accomplishment, or any life-affirming action, dream, or desire. You need this as much as (and sometimes more than) the patient does.

Why? Because you absolutely must find something to like about the patient. Almost anything will do. She collects dolls. He once ran a marathon. She took care of her grandmother in her last days. He once pulled a drowning friend from a raging river. Anything. But something.

Many times suicidal patients will spend most or all of the first few sessions convincing you of what truly burdensome, loathsome creatures they are and, therefore, why they should be permitted to die. Neither you nor the patients can afford to be convinced this is true. All humans have value. Find it and the bonding will begin.

A final thought. Keep in mind that it is the healthy, life-affirming part of the patient that joins with you in the building of a therapeutic alliance. The part that wants to die cannot, and will not, do this. Therefore, for each human connection you are able to make in the building of the relationship, the risk of suicide is directly reduced.

The rule seems to be this: People who are in close, mutually respectful, emotionally solid and safe interpersonal relationships are very unlikely to kill themselves. Job one for therapists: Help the sufferer find, build, and keep such relationships. Let it begin with you.

Therapeutic Suggestions, Strategies, and Techniques

Here, then, is my Whole Earth Catalogue of therapeutic interventions and suggestions that can save lives. Culled from the literature, picked up in lectures, and taught to me by patients, there isn't room here to properly thank everyone.

For the record, there is no single rationale behind all of these techniques. But in each example where I can, I have followed up the suggestion or intervention with an explanation. These interventions are, purposely, not arranged in any order. In some cases, I've given specific interventions a name to better remember them by.

As every therapist is a unique personality, some of these uses of self, questions, schemes, ploys, and angles may not feel right. Fine. Don't use them. But if any of them fit or feel useful, feel free. At least a few should work for just about everyone.

1) *The Placebo Effect.* As with all psychotherapy, the first order of business is to do nothing to foul up your placebo. The patient already believes that you, as a trained counselor, are going to be honest, trustworthy, loyal, and brave. And smart. Smart therapists allow the suffering patient to at least believe he or she is in good hands. This belief is critical to the rekindling of hope. There are many things you can do to foul up your placebo effect (fall asleep, act disinterested, be abrupt, take unimportant phone calls during a session, ask stupid questions, etc.). Don't do these things and you'll be half way home.

Since your office speaks volumes about you, make sure it doesn't wreck your placebo effect. Check it out. Any silly or potentially offensive posters? Anything on the walls or desk that would add to the patient's sense of disillusionment? Does the place exude warmth? A positive mood? Or does the space send off a bureaucratic, we-don't-care-much-about-people chill?

2) *Make a Diagnosis.* The reason people go to professional healers is to get answers. One of the answers they need is to the question, "What's wrong with me?" Therapists and counselors have the power to *name* what is wrong. This power goes with the territory. It is, as my Indian friends would say, big medicine.

A diagnosis can be as formal as, "You have, according the *Diagnostic and Statistical Manual of the American Psychiatric Association*, what we call a Major Affective Disorder." Or, it can be as informal as, "You know what, kid, you're stuck in Blues City."

It is very important to name what you believe to be wrong. This should not be done too quickly. After taking a careful history and usually by the end of the first hour, you will have a pretty good idea about how to name to the problem. You don't have to be sure, but you can say, "I wonder if what is going on is ....?" Just naming the problem does all or most of the following:

- Gives the sufferer the reassurance that, by golly, someone at least knows what's wrong.

- Gives the sufferer some confidence that if the healer knows what's wrong, it can probably be fixed. The upsurge of positive feeling and decrease in felt fear you get from a non-terminal diagnosis is not unlike the relief you feel when a mechanic tells you your car only needed a set of spark plugs, instead of a new engine.

- Reassures the patient that you *heard* what was said. This may be the first clear communication the patient has had with anyone in weeks. Just being heard and understood dramatically reduces feelings of confusion and despair.

The language of diagnosis takes many forms. For some people a formal, medical-sounding statement of what's wrong works best. For other people, something less heady will do the job. A favorite of mine for, say, young men thinking of killing themselves because their girlfriends are leaving them, is, "This is what we call open heart surgery without the benefit of anesthetic." If I get a laugh (however grim), I know I have just accomplished the most important thing a diagnosis does: *separates the sufferer from source of the pain.*

3) *Don't Break the Therapy Frame.* Once you've built a therapeutic alliance, don't violate the frame in which that alliance works. Many suicidal patients have been physically, sexually, and psychologically abused. Such abuse can only take place where there has been no respect for the integrity of the individual's person. The patient may have been violated and victimized many times, so it is essential that the therapist do nothing to make the patient feel used or abused. For example, don't do any of the following:

- Be late for an appointment without a good excuse. This can be interpreted to mean 1) you don't really care about the patient or 2) the patient's time isn't as valuable as yours.

- Go over the allotted time for therapy without checking to see if it's okay.

- Get into any kind of dual relationship. Obviously not sex, but any kind of financial, personal, or social situation in which the patient is meeting your needs instead of the other way around.

- Accept any expensive gifts. Even inexpensive gifts from patients carry invisible price tags. If you don't know what a gift truly costs, find out. It could be to look the other way while the patient goes on to commit suicide.

- Allow a big bill to accumulate if it's a fee-paying patient. Owing a therapist a pile of money is a good reason to stop therapy. A large debt could even be that "last straw" a suicidal person needs to call it quits.

- Let a patient turn you into a therapy god. Flattery from a suicidal patient, at least in my experience, is always a setup for eventual disappointment and possible failure.

Keep the therapy frame clear and fair and free from boundary violations and you will have the best possible working situation for both of you. There may be times to bend the frame a bit, but only with due consideration and after expert consultation and/or supervision.

4) *Empowerment Maneuvers.* If you accept the premise that suicidal people are suicidal, in part anyway, because they feel helpless, hapless, out of control, and powerless, anything the therapist can do to combat these feelings that feed hopelessness will be a plus.

For example, within the context of the therapy itself, here are several things you can do to give the patient a sense of power and control:

- Allow the patient to pick the time of subsequent appointments. You each have schedules, but unless it matters greatly to you, empower the patient to control the time you will meet. Looking at my schedule, I often say, "When's the best day for you?" Or, if things are tight in my schedule, "Is there one time on Thursday that would be better for you than another?"

- Unless, for clinical reasons, you feel strongly about seeing the person alone, invite him or her to bring someone along to a session. In family systems this empowerment move is more complicated, but you can still make some gains here.

- When a patient is obviously unwilling to share right off some deep dark secret, you can shift power and control by saying, "Look, maybe you can't tell me about that right away. That's okay. You can tell me when you feel like it. And I'm sure you will when you can." Except for an active suicide plan, most shameful content can wait.

- If it feels right and is clinically sound, give the patient the power to call you if necessary. Weekends, nights, you work this out together. I make it clear with patients that therapy happens in the office, not on the phone. So I rarely get calls. But I also make it clear I want my patients packing my home phone number, not their pistols.

- Patients on antidepressant medications often would rather not take them. This is a compliance issue and every doctor knows that just because you prescribe some pills, it doesn't mean patients are going to take them. Suicidal people present a special problem here: If they take the pill, it suggests they've decided to live. Some are not ready to make this decision.

  In an effort to empower them (give them control over such things as what goes in their mouth and into their blood streams), I will often say, "Look, these medications work. They'll help you sleep. Your mood will start to improve in ten days or so. You may even get some energy back and begin to feel better. But they won't stop you from killing yourself. Only you can make that decision."

  Note: By giving the power to make the medication decision back to the patient, compliance with "trying" a cure goes way up. It doesn't change our therapy contract one bit, but it communicates very clearly that the patient is, as always, ultimately responsible for his or her own welfare.

Patients can be empowered outside the office as well. If you look at each day as a series of opportunities to make choices (from what socks you pull on in the morning through the last thing you read before going to sleep), then walking folks through these decisions, encouraging them to make different ones (sometimes just for the hell of it), and otherwise showing them that, in fact, they do have *choices* to make every single day, can help them feel stronger and stronger in the personal control department.

It may be helpful to remember that when it comes to some suicide risk factors, none of us has any power over them. Age, sex, race, family history for depression, a medical illness, today's gray and overcast skies, and such are *not* under our control. What is controllable, however, is our attitude toward these givens, our perceptions of them and, most importantly, our ability to reflect on their meaning for us. In many ways, the therapy of suicidal thinking is to bring about a fundamental shift in the patient's perceptions of these givens and, at the same time, to help him or her take personal control over those things that are *not* givens.

In the "not givens" category are things like relationships, jobs, hobbies, food, exercise, and such unkind emotions as jealousy, hatred, revenge, jaded love and, maybe more importantly, how and what we choose to believe is the nature of man and his ultimate purpose. True, some of these are tough and complex subjects, but it has been my experience that suicidal people can benefit greatly by learning to reflect on things philosophical while they re-value their reasons for living, or dying.

Young people haven't had much experience with stopping and thinking a matter through. Therapy can help them do this. Just as you wisely model the thoughtful therapist who questions just how smart killing yourself is, so the adolescent can learn to imitate this style of thinking. Essentially, what needs to be accomplished is nothing less than helping someone become more psychologically minded so that the person can, one day, become his or her own therapist.

The ultimate goal of empowerment maneuvers might be, then, to help the patient feel enough personal control and self reliance to, one day, say to him- or herself, "Ah... this too will pass."

Like a Volkswagen in good working order that you can always count on to get you from point A to point B without breaking down, there is probably no better antidote to the vicissitudes of life than a good working personal philosophy. Therapy, like nothing else, can help a suicidal person find one.

5) *Monitor Your Contract.* No-harm contracts with suicidal people are described in the intervention section. Here, I only wish to remind you that such a contract may need to be updated, modified, or where solid gains are being made in therapy, dropped all together.

Since therapy, like life, is a fluid sort of process where all the twists and turns cannot be anticipated, it is generally a good idea to reinforce the understanding (contract) between the two of you. Simply ask, "So, how are *we* doing? Have you had any suicidal feelings this week? Thoughts?"

Asking this question from time to time does a couple of things: a) lets the patient know you haven't forgotten the reason for the original visit, b) gives you a little added insurance against missing a clue that things may have worsened. This sort of routine checking gives meaning to the contract and keeps it an active part of the treatment plan. If you remember to chart, "Doing okay, not suicidal today," you will have helped document a critical piece of risk management information as well.

6)   *Wedge Driving.* To the suicidal sufferer, psychological pain seems to run in a continuous, seamless flow of awful ideas, uncontrollable thoughts, and wrenchingly painful feelings. A diagnosis that says, "Look, here's what's causing all the suffering" is like driving a wedge into this seamless pain, thus fixing the big problem in one place while the two of you start after the little problems that, having ganged up, are now overwhelming the patient.

By driving wedges in the form of additional diagnostic and fact-finding questions, you can begin to separate the sufferer from his or her pain. This process can also lead to a better understanding of the pain, where it is coming from, and what face it wears. Parse it out, dice it up, make some new sense of the psychic pain and, most likely, the suicidal person will begin to feel better. Here are some handy wedges worth driving:

"This is how depressed people feel, but this is not the real you, is it?" (Affirmation of a positive, earlier self.)

"When you feel this bad, where, exactly, does it hurt?" (Puts a place to the pain and makes it, perhaps, more manageable.)

"If you only think of suicide when you're intoxicated, how is booze your best friend?" (Challenges the role of alcohol in enhancing a depressed mood and growing sense of failure.)

"When you feel the very worst, whose name or face comes to mind?" (May produce a roster of people with whom patient is in conflict and can, thereby, open the door to productive relationship counseling.)

"What finally happened the last time you went through something like this?" (Asks for recall of having survived an earlier crisis.)

"Because your father killed himself, does that mean you have to?" (Challenges the conclusion that heredity begets suicide.)

"Given all that's happened, can you really trust your thoughts just now?" (Helps sufferer accept that, possibly, he or she is not thinking all that well.)

"You seem mad enough to kill yourself; did you make all this anger up yourself?" (Refocuses attention to external sources of frustration and away from self as perpetrator.)

"Do you think it was fair for your mother (father, lover, husband, wife etc.) to cause you this much pain? Or did they really intend to?" (Forces patient to reconsider the motives attributed to others... often erroneously.)

"Given that the kind of pain you are in doesn't last forever, would you advise anyone feeling as miserable as you do right now to kill him- or herself?" (Puts the patient in the role of wise healer, not pained sufferer, thus allowing a direct shift of perspective. The answer here can prove both interesting and therapeutic.)

A good wedge-driving question causes the suicidal person to re-think conclusions already drawn and as the person is gentled along in this question-and-answer format, should create some distance from the pain. The purpose of such questions is to break into the constricted, fixed logic that has led the person to the forever decision. (More of this later in the Socrates Strategy.)

You know you're asking good clinical questions when the suicidal person says things like, "I'm getting confused." Or, "I hadn't thought of it that way." Or falls silent. Getting confused and falling silent to re-think the forever decision is pure gold. I sometimes tell patients I've just tripped up, "You're confused? That's great! Now we're getting someplace."

7) *Never Give Out A Bad Housekeeping Seal of Approval.* At least some chronically suicidal people seem to be looking for professional approval for their suicide. After years of poor coping, repeated losses, and a deep and abiding sense of failure that never seems to pass, some suicidal folks are (often quite openly) looking for someone in authority to say, "I understand. It's okay to kill yourself."

I have even had patients put it to me bluntly, "Why can't I kill myself? Why won't you let me?" I tell them just as bluntly, "Because it isn't my decision and it isn't in my job description."

In a nutshell, I make it very clear that nobody dies on my watch. If they need someone in a position of power to give them permission to kill themselves, they've come to the wrong guy. I don't give out what I call the Bad Housekeeping Seal of Approval—which, as it can be interpreted by patients, means I now agree that they've done such a miserable job of running their lives, they get to stop keeping house altogether. No way.

If the "seal" is given, it is usually given through an unspoken communication from the therapist to the patient. However it happens, the patient comes to believe the therapist no longer believes in his or her survival either. To counter the possibility of this happening, and to avoid becoming an accomplice in a patient's suicide, make up your mind right from the start that nobody dies and everybody lives—at least, and until, something unplanned carries us off.

8) *Be Thoughtfully Active and Confident.* This may seem an obvious prescription, but it isn't. Even though the patient must take ultimate responsibility for his or her life, the therapist must take responsibility for the control of therapy. This means being in charge, asking questions, digging for facts—and scouring the emotional landscape for evidence of change, actions, and reactions. It means listening well and long and never, but never, assuming you know something you don't.

When working with an actively suicidal patient, it is important not to appear ambivalent, uncertain, or wishy-washy about the nature, purpose, and power of therapy. From ancient times up to the present, therapy works. Only the names and faces change. A belief in healing and healers is critical, and suicidal patients who benefit from therapy survive. Therefore, if the therapist is confident about the benefits of therapy, the patient can be more confident about living. Once again, don't do anything to screw up your placebo, and may the Force be with you.

9) *Be Intensely Curious.* I call this the Columbo Technique after Lt. Columbo of TV movie fame. Basically, the notion here is to never let up until you know everything the patient does about his or her reasons for suicide, how he or she intends to pull it off, and what he or she would do to avoid getting caught.

Many times people who have thought long and hard about killing themselves have developed very elaborate plans about how to do it. They know where they will get the gun or pills or rope. They have picked a time and place. They may have written several drafts of suicide notes. But, when the therapist asks after these details, patients give him the *Reader's Digest* version of the plan and skip ahead to other subjects. Don't fall for these evasions.

Rather, circle around and come back to the same question again. And again. And again. Or ask the same question in a slightly different way.

THERAPIST: You said you were going to use a gun... is that your own gun, or your brother's gun?

PATIENT: I didn't say. And what difference does it make?

THERAPIST: Oh, none, I suppose. I was just wondering. Maybe your brother wouldn't give it to you if he knew what you were going to do with it.

PATIENT: He would, too. He knows me, and he respects me. He'd let me do what I have to.

THERAPIST: Is your brother's gun a magnum, or a little .22?

PATIENT (growing testy): Say, why are you so interested in my brother's gun? My suicide is my business.

But it isn't his business, not now that he's sitting in your office. And, because of your Lt. Columbo, never-say-die questioning, you now know several things you didn't know if you'd have allowed the patient to put you off—not the least of which is where the murder weapon is and who might help us save this chap's life.

The way I see it is like this: curiosity only kills cats, not therapists. And it is curiosity that can save a life by stopping a murder before it happens.

10) *Grant Permission to Live.* However it comes about psychologically, some suicidal people feel they have been ordered to die, or are, by reason of having reached some specified criteria, now obliged to die. Here are several ways to explore and say to a suicidal patient he or she does not *have* to suicide:

- "Who expects you to die?"

- "Is it written down somewhere that you have to die?"

- "Where did you get the notion that when such and such happens, you're supposed to kill yourself?"

You can undo this sort of negative outcome thinking with:

- "I want you to know, in no uncertain terms, that it's okay with me if you live."

- "No one has the right to expect you to end your life so theirs can be easier."
- "You certainly have my permission to go on living."
- " I don't know about anybody else, but I want you to live. In fact, I insist on it!"

Suicidal people of all ages respond to this granting of permission to live, but maybe especially the young and the old. The effect, when I've personally seen it take hold, is often like granting a reprieve to someone expecting to be hanged on the morrow.

11) *Cognitive Monkey-Wrenching.* Much like the wedge-driving questions outlined earlier, cognitive monkey-wrenching is a way to invade and then disrupt the patient's suicidal thoughts and plans by putting yourself right in the middle of them.

It is well to remember that suicidal ideation is often a friend, not an enemy. It is the one place suicidal people can go where they can still feel some sense of control. Even relief. Let a therapist into these calming reflections and they will never be the same. In a word, cognitive monkey-wrenching is a method of desecrating the chapel in which death is worshiped.

To get a monkey wrench into the works, you begin by prying into the patient's thoughts with detailed questions about the whole experience of suicidal thinking and feeling (á la Lt. Columbo). Once you know as much about the plan to die as the patient does, it is very easy to toss a wrench into the works. Here are some very good wrenches that have worked for me.

- "Gee, the next time you're down by the river watching the water and wondering what it would be like to slip quietly under the waves, I wonder if you'll hear my voice asking, 'Are you sure this is such a hot idea?' It could come from right behind you."

RESULT: The patient's once perfect suicide plan has just had a monkey wrench tossed into the middle of it. Plan A, jumping in the river, is never going to be the same again.

or,

- "You know how you like to sit and stare into the candles just before you take out that little razor you keep in the drawer by your bed to cut on your wrists? Well, I hope this smiling face of mine doesn't suddenly appear in the flames."

RESULT: The patient's self-hypnotic induction to an episode of life-threatening behavior, and the comfort she derived from warm blood flowing over her arms, is no longer an exclusive club of one. A party crasher has ruined everything.

Note: You know you've jammed things up if the patient gets upset with you for tossing in a monkey wrench. Generally, non-impulsive suicidal people don't like you or anyone else mucking around in their suicidal ideations. These are, like garden paths and quiet churches, mental retreats used for respite from seamless suffering.

In my own experience, several patients have become visibly angry right after realizing my smiling face was going to pop up the next time they started thinking about killing themselves. But that's okay. People get over anger; it's death they seem to have so much trouble with.

12) *Give Permission to Think and Feel.* Always consider the strong possibility that the suicidal person in front of you has never known, nor felt allowed to feel, the full range of his or her own feelings and thoughts. Most of what therapists do in therapy is to name and normalize what the sufferer believes does not have a name and is, therefore, abnormal. What is nameless produces fear; what is thought to be abnormal produces shame.

To reduce anxiety, fear, and shame, all you have to do is give implicit and explicit permission for the sufferer to *say* what he or she has already *thought* and to *express* what he or she has already *felt*.

Like wanting to kill a husband, for example. Or wishing your whole family would die in a fiery crash. Or hating your homosexual feelings so much you want to cut off your penis. Or being afraid that if you start crying you will never be able to stop. Therapists simply must give permission for these thoughts to be said, felt, and validated so that they can come into the light of common human understanding.

Of course it helps if you're not easily shocked, have a touch of gray hair, and are not much surprised by the full range of human behavior—no matter how odd, bizarre, strange, or crazy some act, feeling, or thought may appear. My advice is that if you are just starting out in this business and find yourself amazed by some unusual revelation (e.g., as a boy, the person had sex with a dog), try not to tumble backward out of your chair... it unnerves the patient.

13) *Involve the Family.* As noted elsewhere, suicide almost always involves significant others. Sometimes the suicidal person is striking back at loved ones for abuse received or rejection perceived; at other times there are enmeshed, clinging, symbiotic systems of longstanding pathology in which the only way a person can get out of the sick family system is through suicide. There may be shameful family secrets, prohibitions against anyone stepping outside of the family system for help, and all sorts of dark struggles going on among the players. To deal only with the identified patient in such systems is to severely limit your effectiveness and, into the bargain, limit your ability to lower suicide risk.

In working with suicidal children (of any age if they are still living in the home), ask yourself the following question: What would happen to the parents if this child grew up and left?

If your answer proves problematic (the parents would probably divorce, mother would sicken and die, father would lose his psychological wife, etc.), then you know, right off, that family therapy is probably indicated. To the extent the family's role is to raise up its offspring into healthy, autonomous adults, its failure to do so is an indication something is wrong. Growing up shouldn't mean disloyalty, abandoning your mom to an abusive husband or intolerable loneliness, or otherwise putting the family in some sort of psychological jeopardy. And if it does, something is very wrong.

While this is not the place to detail the ins and outs of good family systems therapy (see readings section for Joseph Richman's excellent book on this subject), it is important to know just how your patient's suicidality fits into the family belief structure and what consequences his or her suicide would have on others. Insofar as suicide solves, quite permanently, all of the patient's problems of separation anxiety, conflicted communications with parental figures, and enmeshment struggles, the temptation to exit a sick family via suicide is often a very tempting one.

While it is possible to work with only the identified patient from such a family, the better part of clinical judgment would be to get everyone together, get them all to make a commitment to safety, and then set the ground rules for how the therapy will proceed. If you're already a family therapist, you know what to do; if you're not, get some training, a consult, read a few books, and dive in.

14) *Keep Shame at Bay.* Especially with adolescents and adults raised in shame-based families, it is critical that when you give permission for the expression of thoughts and feelings, you keep shame at arm's length. Feelings of worthlessness, humiliation, and shame are often internalized statements by one or both parents whose techniques of child management were based on the notion that a properly shamed child is a properly behaved one.

A person raised in shame (you guessed it) will plan a very proper suicide. The plan will be discreet and tidy. All due attention will have been paid to matters of propriety: how the deed will be done, the appearance of the corpse, timely notifications and, sometimes, prearranged funeral matters.

With such terribly shamed patients, it is critical not to allow even a whisper of shame or condemnation to escape your own lips or actions. Because if you do, the patient will almost invariably retreat from the session and put the cork back into that bottle in which he or she keeps those dreadful (read, shameful) feelings.

Even with grown, intelligent, successful adults, you will often find suicide and shame powerfully linked together. Almost always from a dysfunctional family of origin, shame remains a driving force in the suicidal person's desire to die. Some parents, it seems, are able to instill these killer, almost post-hypnotic suggestions into their children before they've even developed much language, let alone any self-esteem or ability to fight back. Our job, then, is to root out these killer implants, lay them on a heavy table in a good light, and smash them with a big shovel.

For example, I once worked with a professional man whose main message from his cold and distant father was, "If you ever do anything to shame this family, you'll know what you have to do." Always a "dirty and worthless little bastard" (his father's words), there was never any question in this man's mind about what he would, one day, eventually have to do. Undoing this curse by investigating the roots of shame he experienced as a boy was the whole of therapy. Helping such a man understand and accept that, as the poet said, we come through our parents, not from them, can be life saving.

In my own experience, it does little good to direct a frontal assault on a shaming parent, especially if the parent is still alive, in the same town, or out in the waiting room. Blood is thicker than water—at least in the beginning of therapy. It is your gentle questioning, unstinting support, and belief in the process of separation and individuation that will, over time, lead to a change in self perception and enough self-esteem to make a parentectomy possible.

15) *Reframing.* In many situations, suicide is the solution to a problem over which the patient simply wants more control. While not as lethal in terms of overall risk (the patient only wants more power and influence, not death), the forever decision can be reframed (restated) in ways similar to these examples:

FRAME: A girl says she wants to kill herself because boyfriend is leaving her.

REFRAME: "It sounds like you would like more control over him. Maybe be able to make him do something he doesn't want to do."

FRAME: A man wants to kill himself because his wife wants a divorce and his business is failing.

REFRAME: "If you could save the business, would you still need to die?"

or,

"If your wife would come back, you'd have more control over things and could then get the business back on its feet."

FRAME: A teenaged boy has just been arrested. He's failing school and was sent home from class the day before. Already depressed and miserable and frightened, he says he would rather die than face his father.

REFRAME: "It sounds as though you're afraid your father will punish you. If you felt a little stronger and knew better how he might handle this, would you feel less frightened about what might happen?"

In general, reframing translates the wish to die into the wish for more control. Reframing allows the patient to understand that suicide is an escapist solution to what seems like an impossible and uncontrollable future.

Note: In cases where suicide represents a need for more control, suicide is truly a pseudosolution. Pointing this out again and again can reorient the person's thinking and lead to better problem solving.

16) *The "Back to the Couch" Technique.* This intervention was taught to me by a very special, chronically suicidal patient who invariably waited until the end of the therapy hour to let me know she was going to leave my office, go home, and kill herself. She had several ways to let me know this. One of my favorites was, "You've been awfully kind to me these past months. I'll call and schedule another appointment sometime next week."

This was a lie. We had a standing appointment. She had no intention of calling me. Her smile and brightened mood was a dead giveaway. Despite her words, she was sending a coded message that translated to, "Thanks for trying, but I've decided to go ahead and get it over with."

On correctly interpreting this message, I would march her back to couch and start all over again. My next patient might have to wait, but this one wasn't leaving until she was feeling properly miserable again—miserable, but re-committed to therapy for at least another week.

Here's the back-to-the-couch rule: *Challenge every veiled threat.* Studies indicate the majority of therapists whose patients killed themselves in treatment did not know their patients were suicidal at the time they died. That means that most of us can be lulled into believing patients are no longer at risk when, in fact, they are. This false sense of security is just that: a false sense of security.

Therefore, let nothing slip by. If you query a suicidal person too much about their suicidality and get a "Gee, you're more worried about my suicide risk than I am," so what? You can always apologize and say, "Because I like you, I'm just double checking."

17) *Anticipate Times of Increased Risk.* Over the sometimes long haul of therapy, there are events which pop up, planned and unplanned, that may increase the patient's stress and vulnerability to suicide. These are generally life events over which the patient feels increasingly less or no control. Anticipate these risk windows, bring them into the therapy work, and otherwise be prepared to manage them aggressively. A partial list of such risk windows would include:

- The final realization that a much wanted relationship is truly ended.
- A best friend moves away.

- Being fired from a job, especially where the person was emotionally and psychologically dependent on the job for a sense of self-worth and identity.

- A therapist retires, moves away, or takes another job that requires the end of a therapy relationship.

- Any return to drinking, including a single drinking episode (see Alcohol in Special Topics).

- Completing any inpatient or residential drug or alcohol treatment program. Clean and sober, the world can suddenly seem awfully ugly and unacceptable. Worse, all the problems that made addiction seem like a pretty good idea are still there to be solved.

- Discharge from a psychiatric hospital (for the same reasons as above).

- Any loss, real or imagined, that the patient perceives to be unacceptable.

Basically, the wise therapist anticipates as many unforeseen slings and arrows of outrageous fortune as possible and tries to prepare the patient to deal with these either before they happen, while they are happening, or immediately afterward. Sometimes this will require extra sessions.

It is often valuable to ask the patient the following question: What could possibly happen in the future that would make you feel suicidal again? Talking these possibilities through (and what the two of you are going to do if and when any of these things happen) can help inoculate the patient against another episode of suicidality.

18) *The Eye of the Storm.* It is well known that many suicidal people feel a wonderful sense of relief once they decide, for real, to kill themselves. Their faces often resemble the beatific smile of the Buddha. To the therapist whose patient has been struggling (mostly unsuccessfully) to get a grip on the problems he or she has been preparing to die to solve, when you see this smile, this sudden chipperness, this apparent overnight shift from misery to peace, *now is the time to hit the panic button!*

This must be done immediately. Any of the following questions will do:

- "You look awfully happy today; can you tell me why?"

- "Yesterday you were miserable; today you seem so calm. Do you know something I don't?"

- "Have you made up your mind to kill yourself?"

The best place to ask these questions is in the office, but any place will do. If you can hear this calm over the phone, ask over the phone. But whatever you do, you must get the person back on the couch, back into therapy, and back into the struggles shared by the rest of us.

The work of therapy is seldom easy for suicidal people. Sometimes, after several weeks of long, difficult, and seemingly unproductive work in therapy, the patient will (without letting you know) decide to give it up. But because the patient owes you the courtesy, he or she will keep one last appointment. It is on this appointment when the patient's mood may appear so much better. Therefore, *beware the happy patient!*

19) *Script Analysis.* Early on in therapy, one of the first jobs I undertake with patients is to examine, in minute detail, just where they got the idea that suicide was an acceptable solution to life's problems in the first place. As a basic belief, its origin must be found. And once found, the validity of this belief must be challenged, chipped away at, pestered, and otherwise turned upside down and around until, in the fresh context of a new perspective, the patient at least has the chance to toss it aside as a bum idea.

Fundamentally, the unexamined belief that, for example, "If things don't work out, I can always kill myself" does not materialize out of thin air; it comes from a human source. That source can be a parent, a relative, a friend, or even a movie or book. If you are a disgraced Samurai warrior, the source is cultural and you've always known what to do when the going gets really shameful. In the case of Ernest Hemingway, his father scripted him to suicide when his father shot himself while Ernest was still a youth. The themes of death and suicide haunted the writer all his days.

There are whole books written on the business of script analysis, but here are my suggestions on how to use the analogy of the life script to probe and challenge this fundamental, and most dangerous belief:

• Introduce the analogy that life can be like a play—a play with a beginning, middle, and end. Ask the patient where in the play we are as we sit and talk. Act I, scene 2? Act III, scene 3?

- Confirm that we already know this play is closer to a tragedy than a comedy. Then ask if the play started out this way, or did it change along the way? If it changed, when did it change?
- Now ask who's writing this play? The patient? His mother? Her father? And who in the hell wrote into the script that part that the patient must suicide somewhere toward the end of Act II?

The answer to these questions may tell you who set the stage for the tragedy and who outlined the first draft of the suicide script. This script and its original author must be examined and challenged. If this is a parent (and too often it is), the patient may feel protective and even defensive that you would dig up the dead and begin to argue about this legacy. But in my view, that's exactly what you must do.

However implanted in the script, the belief that one must die, one day, by suicide is just that: *a belief.* Merely a human curse, it is not a reality. It is not destined. Death by suicide is a requirement for none of us—no matter who wrote the script.

Also, keep in mind that the strength with which beliefs are held varies over time. One hundred years ago the percent of belief that man could walk on the moon approached zero (Jules Verne was a holdout). Fifty years ago the man-on-moon belief was, maybe, 50%. Now everybody believes with 100% certainty that a man can walk on the moon. This same fluid, ever-changing strength of belief goes on with suicidal people, too.

In the beginning of therapy with someone "scripted" to die by suicide, the belief system supporting death by one's own hand may approach 90%. As therapy goes on, however, the belief in a long and happy life terminated by natural causes may rise from 10% to 50%—resulting, usually, in a corresponding decrease in the percent of belief in an early suicidal death.

Interestingly, these belief systems are not necessarily attached in the brain. Or at least they don't seem to be. I have even had a patient's percentage belief in life increase dramatically, only to then say, "Well, this is all fine and dandy, but if she leaves me again I'll have to kill myself."

The job, as I see it, is to raise up the one belief system while lowering the other. If I can tie the two together through a careful analysis of the script, root out the source of the forever decision, and get some psychological distance from the curse, then I feel much better about accomplishing my main mission: *to get the patient to take over rewriting his or her own life script.*

This approach, by the way, can be empowering. But it can also be frightening. Many patients have never seen themselves as the authors of their own lives. Getting them to take on this awesome responsibility is seldom a snap. Still, if you work at it—and they stay with you—this quantum leap in assuming personal control over the rest of their lives can be nothing short of miraculous. Because, once you realize you don't have to die by your own hand, and the worst anyone can ever do is kill you, the sky's the limit.

20) *Pushing Past Death.* This technique is one to be used very cautiously. But, depending on the relative risks and the strength of the therapy relationship, it can sometimes prove very helpful to push patients past their projected suicide and have them imagine a future without them in it. Too often, patients will only have considered the immediate relief death promises for themselves, not the pain and suffering their death will cause others.

The risk in using a patient's ability to spin a death scenario beyond demise is that, sometimes, the pain others will surely experience is precisely the desired result. But this finding can be useful in therapy—just so long as you are prepared to reframe this desire to hurt others into something more healthy: i.e., a need for more control, a need to get more love and attention from others, a need for more understanding, whatever.

The biggest problem with this technique is that if you are working with a patient who feels he or she is a "burden" to others, and suicide would make life so much simpler for the survivors, you will have to work very hard and quickly to bring about some fundamental change in the patient's real or imagined social environment. The patient's perception of being a burden to others may be wrong but, sometimes, you will find exactly what you hope you won't find: Nobody really likes or wants or can care for this person after all.

Still, by asking the patient to talk about what effect the suicide will have on others, at least you have a chance to understand the underlying motivation for such a desperate business. Here, then, are some of the results pushing past death may produce:

- The patient is brought up close and personal to the finality of death. This can sometimes bring an element of reality testing into the patient's escapist fantasies, and can be especially helpful with youth.

- The patient is forced to reconsider his or her "real" motives for suicide. To hurt others? To unburden significant others? To provide an insurance death benefit to the children? To avoid some terrible shame or confrontation? What?

- By imaging the lives of friends and family well past the funeral (weeks? months? years?), the patient must deal with the possibility that the current crisis is, in the long scheme of life, temporary in nature.

In the few times I have used this intervention, I have done so when other modes of countering the patient's desire to die were not working. I have not found, by the way, that fear of the hereafter, or God's anger, or the possibility that nothingness begins with death, or what have you, has been much of a deterrent to suicide. If anything, it is our responsibilities on *this* side of the grave that help keep people alive—a fact I am not above using if I have to get someone's attention.

For example, in the case of parents who say, "The kids would be better off without me," I simply confront this goofy idea by reminding them that this conclusion is simply not true, never can be true, and never will be true. Not only will they have left a psychological curse as a legacy, but they will have ducked their very real emotional, psychological, social, and financial responsibilities to help the kids finish school, help them get some additional training or a college education, and see them through their marriage, first children, and so on.

Again, the prerequisites for such a powerful confrontation are a very solid therapeutic alliance; a healing context; and enough time on the therapy clock to deal thoroughly with the quite predictable rage, anger, guilt, and grief.

Some might feel this approach is harsh, too dangerous, or too guilt-inducing. Maybe it is. But there are times when, if nothing else is working, grounding the future in a firm reality can have powerful effects on the pseudosolution of suicide. You are not, by the way, making any of this projected reality up. As a trained therapist and reasonably alert and sober person, you can pretty well lay out how things will be for those left behind. For the person who kills him- or herself, one thing is very sure: He or she won't be around to see how life turns out. These are the facts. So, is there any good reason why the suicidal sufferer shouldn't know them too?

21) *Socrates When You Need Him.* Often the best tool for the therapist working on the negative, distorted, and confused cognitions of the suicidal person is Socratic dialogue—roughly defined as a method of teaching by asking enough simple questions to lead the student to a certain conclusion.

Rather than tell his students what to think, Socrates simply asked them questions until they discovered some truth or other for themselves. Ask enough good questions and, sooner or later, the suicidal person will be drawn to a conclusion other than the forever one.

Here is how such a dialogue might have proved useful in a typical situation involving man being left by a woman he does not want to lose.

THERAPIST: Why do you think she rejected you?

PATIENT: They always reject me. Didn't I make it clear? I'm selfish and stupid.

THERAPIST: Have you always been selfish and stupid?

PATIENT: Yes.

THERAPIST: With everyone, or only with women?

PATIENT: Hummm. Maybe more with women.

THERAPIST: *Maybe* more with women?

PATIENT: Well, once in awhile I can be pretty generous.

THERAPIST: Like when?

PATIENT: I once gave an old fiance' an expensive diamond.

THERAPIST: What happened to her?

PATIENT: It didn't work out. I found somebody else.

THERAPIST: What happened to the ring?

PATIENT: I let her keep it. I'm not stingy.

THERAPIST: Let me get this straight: *You* left her, she didn't leave you? And you let her keep the ring?

PATIENT: Yes.

THERAPIST: And you didn't become suicidal?

PATIENT: That's right. I mean, I was leaving her, wasn't I?

THERAPIST: Then, women don't always reject you. In fact, sometimes you reject women?

PATIENT: Say..., are you trying to trip me up?

Depending on the quality of the therapeutic relationship, the therapist might now say something like, "You old heartbreaker, you. You've left a few yourself, haven't you? And being a big-hearted guy, you let the last one keep the ring?" Such an interpretation would help cement the following facts:

- Women do not *always* leave him (misperception, distortion of fact, and erroneous conclusion).

- He is not a *perfectly* rejectable person (second erroneous conclusion).

- He is not *always* selfish and stupid (third erroneous conclusion).

In sum, while he's been hurt, the wound is not fatal; he does not *have* to die.

The purpose of Socratic questioning is to draw out the inconsistencies in logic based on wrong facts which lead to the forever decision. Like our fictional man in the above dialogue, if you are *always* rejectable because you are *always* selfish and stupid and can *never* make *any* relationship work with *any* women, then, according to our conclusion here, any decent fellow *ought* to do the decent thing and just shoot himself.

Here are three keys to getting good results with the Socratic method:

- Never embarrass the person you're questioning. He or she already feels stupid enough. (Keep shame at bay.)

- Unless forced to the wall, let the person draw his or her own conclusions from your questions. These self-discoveries are much more valuable to the patient than any conclusion you can share. More, making these self-discoveries will increase self-esteem.

- Each time the patient draws a new conclusion and makes a life-positive statement, write it down in your notes, put quote marks around it, and then circle the quote. Later, when the patient is back in the low self-esteem soup, you can read back to him or her something you recorded last week.

For example, the patient may say, "Sometimes I don't get my facts straight, so maybe I'm not such a bad person after all." Or, "People used to really like me before I met Christy... maybe she changed me for the worse." Or, "I've done a few good things with my life, and some of them have been pretty darned wonderful."

To combat the logic for suicidal death and to improve the patient's chance for survival, you need all the positive self-statements you can extract. Bringing such statements up again and again throughout the course of therapy can give the patient strength in the same way a well-considered compliment makes you feel all warm and fuzzy on the inside. More importantly, such self-affirmations will help the patient shift back to a positive self-image compatible with life and incompatible with death.

As Socrates might ask, "Now that we know you are basically a decent, thoughtful, caring human being who only occasionally draws wrong conclusions from questionable facts, does it make sense to put such a person to death?"

22) *Confront False Pride (but gently).* Suicide is sometimes a tool people use to keep what they have. For example, if you are willing to die to keep your reputation, then you'd best hope you never get caught doing something truly shameful. Several studies have clearly documented that in the drought-ravaged Midwest during the 1990s, dozens of farmers took their own lives rather than "lose the family farm."

The point is that ending one's own life can be an issue of pride. And while sometimes this makes sense (especially for political or military leaders who make horrendous blunders), it is ordinary false pride that can lead to unnecessary suicides.

A common example is the macho man who says, "I'm not the kind of man women leave. If someone is going to leave, it's me! Now where's my shotgun!?" Suicide, in this context, becomes a very powerful tool to blackmail others into re-thinking their positions. The statement is clear: I will not accept life on these terms.

The "terms" can include ill health, being rejected by a lover, being fired, losing a ton of money on the stock market, getting an F on a college term paper, or even being sent home from school. True, these are probably last straws in otherwise suicide-susceptible people, but the issues of pride and anticipated shame can loom very large in the reasons behind the suicide.

Confrontation of false pride must be done, but it must be done gingerly and only in the context of an extremely good therapeutic relationship. More importantly, such people (especially men) must be left with sufficient pride to save face. This is tricky and, frankly, I have no simple formula for pulling it off. But having worked several months with a retired Army officer who kept sticking a .45 automatic pistol in his mouth every time things didn't go his way, I can tell you that, in the end, it was humor that saved us.

After several weeks of white-knuckle therapy with this powerful, stern, prideful man I remarked that it seemed sort of silly to me that if his wife wanted to move on, why he should go down with a sinking ship. The major quickly corrected me that it was sailors who went down with their ships, not soldiers. Having told him earlier I'd been an E-4 in the Army, he laughed and said, "Ah! What can you expect from enlisted swine!" Then he laughed... at himself. With a capacity to see himself as absurd, and now separated a few paces from his pain and the terms he was unwilling to accept, I knew I could help him live.

23) *Self-disclosure.* The whole subject of disclosing something about yourself to a patient in the course of therapy is controversial. Some say you should never do it, others say you should never *not* do it. When it comes to working with suicidal people, self-disclosure is an even more dicey decision. Unfortunately, suicidal people will often ask, "Have you ever thought about killing yourself?"

Strictly a personal opinion, I offer this advice:

- If a patient asks right away if you've ever thought of taking your own life, tell the truth. To my knowledge, lying by either party never helped any therapy relationship. If you choose to use the old therapist stall, "I don't think that's an appropriate question," you will, in my opinion, run the risk of having an already low-down feeling person feel even more low-down for having asked an inappropriate question. You may also have risked the development of trust.

- If you have given suicide serious consideration at some time in your life, sharing just as many of the details as to not let the therapy hour become your therapy hour may prove helpful. It will even be more helpful if you got some of the same kind of help you're now giving. The message, "See, therapy works!," is a very powerful and hopeful one.

   Of course, the risk is that the suicidal person (upon learning you too have been suicidal) may think, "Jeeze, isn't anyone sane anymore?" To handle such a self-disclosure well, you must anticipate this increased fear, address it, and talk it through with the goal of reinforcing the human connection through even greater candor and trust.

Finally, I'll remind you about the therapist conditions I reviewed in the beginning of this section and how important it is to be squared away on your own suicide status before doing this work.

24) *What's the Worst That Could Happen?* More a series of questions than a technique, this line of inquiry takes the patient's present formulation of the dilemma and, by obliging an answer to the question (What's the worst that could happen?), carries him or her past the present conclusion (suicide) and into the very things that may be driving the desire to die.

PATIENT: She's leaving and I won't stand for it.

THERAPIST: What's the worst that could happen if she left?

PATIENT: She can't leave!

THERAPIST: I understand how you feel, but what's the worst that could happen if she did leave?

PATIENT: I'd... I'd be lost.

THERAPIST: Then what's the worst that could happen?

PATIENT: I... I... I don't think I can live without her.

THERAPIST: But if she left, and you had to live without her, what's the worst that could happen?

PATIENT: I'd be alone.

THERAPIST: Yes, you'd be alone. And a little lost, like you were before you met her. Now, then, once you were alone, what's the worst that could happen?

PATIENT: I hate being alone. But if I had to be alone... well, I guess I'd have to be. For awhile anyway.

The idea here is to get suicidal people to project a future beyond the unacceptable one in which they find themselves. To the degree suicide is an escape from an intolerable, psychologically painful, and hopeless situation, imagining oneself beyond that situation can revive hope.

Because the future is where fear lies (I'll be lost, alone, frightened, miserable, etc.), patients often need a little shove into that future. In their minds (and you can check this out with a few simple questions), they've been tip-toeing up to that fear-filled future, taking a peek at it, and then backing quietly away—thus unconsciously reinforcing thoughts of suicide by reducing the anxiety aroused as they steal glimpses of the face of fear. Like a kid watching a horror movie, they keep their face covered with their hands and peek through their fingers. Our job is to get their hands down from their face and show them that fear doesn't kill.

By gently asking this question again and again, you lead patients to face their worst fears. In a kind of branching logic into an unknown future that *excludes* suicide, the two of you will likely stumble upon something not only endurable, but even hopeful.

If you meet resistance to this life-saving question, you can just say, "Look, we know suicide will take you beyond any situation and far beyond any fear. And, for a fact, you won't have to solve any more problems, feel any more pain, or face any more uncertainties. But what would happen if you lived? I mean, what's the worst that could happen?"

25) *Plan B.* I use Plan B all the time with all sorts of patients, including suicidal ones. The notion here, in a nutshell, is that whatever the patient has been doing (Plan A) hasn't been working very well—and usually

not at all. Once I have a good history and can sum up for the patient what I think has been going on that has led him or her to the forever decision, I then describe the fix the patient is in and agree that the situation is both impossible and hopeless. This amounts to agreeing with the negative side of the patient's ambivalence which, interestingly enough, often leads to a sigh and a comment, "Thank God, someone finally understands."

Once I have a nod of agreement (yes, that's the way it is, doc), then I say, "Okay. Now, that's Plan A. What's Plan B?"

"Plan B?"

"Yes. Now don't tell me you've gone along all these years working Plan A without a backup plan? You know, a Plan B—what you were going to do if Plan A didn't work out."

"Huh?"

The fact is, many people do not have a Plan B. We just muddle through life working Plan A. Plan A can be that job you always wanted at the factory, taking over the family farm, becoming a doctor, marrying your high school sweetheart, whatever. This is fine and, if the world were perfectly just and fair and the "rain don't fall and the creek don't rise," we'd all get to live Plan A. Unfortunately, bad stuff happens. And this is where we need a Plan B.

Most suicidal people do not have a Plan B. In fact, I've yet to meet my first suicidal patient who had a Plan B, let alone a Plan C. This may be characteristic of suicidal people, but I haven't met them all yet and my sample is quite small.

Together with all the usual and customary losses and setbacks and disappointments life hands us, all it takes for Plan A to go up in smoke is for the factory to close, a drought to bankrupt the family farm, the practice of medicine to become impossibly stressful, and/or your high school sweetheart to leave you for someone else. With Plan A in ashes, what's a person to do?

What you do is put together Plan B. Plan B can be *anything*. It doesn't have to be realistic but, as you go along putting wheels under the plan with the patient, Plan B often begins to look more and more viable.

To get patients unfrozen from their decision to die, I tell them that they do not have to actually live out Plan B, but that they at least owe it to themselves to *imagine* what living it out might be like. Spinning scenarios into unknowable futures is something only human beings can do; getting suicidal people to this can free them up like nothing else I've ever tried. (This is also a good time and place to work in a few "What's the Worst That Could Happen" questions.)

Yes, some will resist and say "Oh, this isn't real. I could never...(fill in here with any of 101 "reasonable" excuses)."

To which I say, "Sure. I understand all that. And we can keep plugging away at Plan A. But what's the harm in dreaming?"

My experience with helping people work up a Plan B has been that, once they have any sort of backup plan at all, their felt tension and sense of impending doom begins to evaporate as quickly as getting an 11th-hour reprieve from the Governor that, having reconsidered, your noon execution has been cancelled. Like those spirited prisoners who keep hope alive by actively scheming, dreaming, and working on Plan B (the escape), so too can suicidal people keep hope alive imagining a life other than the one they are willing to die to get out of. The effect here, by the way, is often quite dramatic.

26) *Dreams on the Shelf.* This area of inquiry goes along with helping folks develop a Plan B. Basically, it involves the notion that all of us, when we were young, had dreams. These dreams might have been to be a forest ranger, a rocket scientist, a lawyer, a painter, a maker of fine jewelry, a stand-up comic, a writer of songs or poetry or novels. It doesn't matter what the dream was—only that we once dreamed it.

They say that without your dreams you die and, certainly, once you kill yourself, you forsake all your dreams—even the ones you never tried to live. By your act of self-destruction, you say, in effect, I give up *all* my dreams.

But wait a minute. Before you die, could you tell us what those dreams were? What did you really want to be when you grew up? What wild and crazy thing did you always want to do that you won't ever do once you're dead? What promises did you make to yourself that, someday, you'd finally have the guts or the time to try? If you kill yourself who, then, will live those dreams?

Put in the form of a question, what I try to learn from suicidal people is what dreams they will leave on the shelf. This questioning often leads to grief for noble deeds never done, mountains never climbed, rivers never crossed, words never spoken, and songs never sung. But that's okay. Because once we're in touch with the sorrow of what could have been, we can start to reach for the joy of what still might be.

I begin this intervention with something like, "Remember back when you were a kid? The way you dreamed about growing up? Remember what you really wanted to be, or something you always wanted to do? Did you ever promise yourself that, someday, you'd do.... what? What was it?"

If I get resistance ("It's too late for me," "I'm too old to start over," etc., etc.), I remind them that Colonel Sanders didn't start frying his own Kentucky Fried Chicken until he got his first Social Security check at age 65 and that, if it weren't for second chances, there wouldn't be any chances at all. Besides, we're all going to die anyway, so why not dust off one of those old dreams and give it a whirl?

This should be a gentle, but persistent challenge. I use the image of the dreams kept high on a shelf where nobody can find them but the dreamer. The dream, written on a slip of paper and rolled up in a red ribbon, has been secreted away because others thought it foolish, or immature, or unrealistic, or even stupid. Together with the patient, we dust off the dream to see if, just for the hell of it, maybe we ought to just go ahead and live it.

27) *The Teddy Bear Ploy.* Research suggests that people who have responsibility for the welfare of others (especially children) are less likely to commit suicide. You can't, if you are a reasonably thoughtful and caring person, just go off and kill yourself and leave those who are dependent on you to fend for themselves.

This need to be needed should, in my view, never be underestimated. And, although a dicey and sometimes risky intervention to make, I have, where I can, tried to make suicidal people see themselves as *needed* by others—sometimes by gently banging away at their erroneous belief that no one needs them or, more actively, getting them into situations where they simply must get out of themselves and into the life of someone else. Volunteering in a nursing home, for example, or buying lunch for a homeless person. In one case, I made a suicidal father sit down and actually calculate the true cost of his children's college education; he learned that, for a fact, his $50,000 life insurance money wouldn't get them past their sophomore years.

From a favorite Shanahan *New Yorker* cartoon of mine, two policemen are trying to talk a suicidal teddy bear in from a high-rise ledge. One of the officers is saying, "There's an Officer Ripley in here who could use a hug." And we know, instantly, that the teddy bear cannot, now, jump. Reminded of his prime function, his suicide becomes impossibly selfish.

Even though most suicidal people are too preoccupied with their own pain and suffering to think of others, the fact remains that their hugs are still very much in demand. Everywhere you look people are hug-deprived: children, parents, friends, old folks in nursing homes, cocaine babies, the homeless, teddy bears—you name them and they could probably stand a hug. Even stray cats could use a hug, and I'm not fond of cats.

Therefore, once I have a working relationship with suicidal persons, I often try to unwrap the arms they've been holding themselves with and get them wrapped around someone else. Why? Because hugged creatures hug back—cats, of course, being the exception.

It also helps for suicidal people to set their own misery aside long enough to gain some perspective on the relative merits of their crisis. Cheap comparisons, e.g., "You think *you've* got it bad...," seldom work early in therapy, but later on they can prove very helpful to get suicidal people to lend a hand to others in need. Given the chance, most of us learn rather quickly that, once we put all our big problems on the table next to everybody else's big problems, we would, after looking everything over and asked to take our pick, just as soon have our own *little* problems back—thank you very much. This quantitative shift in perspective can often help the sufferer find a way to be needed, useful, wanted, and yes, even loved in this human community of ours.

28) *Right Person, Wrong Place.* Many times suicidal people find themselves in what they believe to be impossible situations. And sometimes they are right. There are, given certain personality types, impossible situations, impossible relationships, impossible jobs, and toxic living conditions. You can, in a word, be the

right person in the wrong place. But you don't have to kill yourself to get out.

The Right Person, Wrong Place technique involves first getting a good right-hand grip on the type of person you are working with. For example, is this person artistic, creative, and free-spirited, or meticulous, over-controlled, and mechanical? If the former, she is not going to have much fun turning nuts on bolts for General Motors; if the latter, he is not going to enjoy supervising some newspaper's creative arts department. The question that needs answering is this: Does *this* person fit into *this* place?

A variation of the old round peg in the square hole problem, many suicidal people have been living and working for years in situations and relationships antithetical to their needs, personalities, and dreams. As a result, they've become depressed and hopeless. Allowing them to consider that, just possibly, they are an okay person caught up in not okay circumstances allows them a way out.

By affirming that the patient is okay (right person), but simply trapped in a bad situation (wrong place), all sorts of things become possible. Not only does the patient get to keep his or her self-esteem (or what's left of it), but some of the blame for pain and suffering can be shifted to the W.P. (wrong place).

For example, the statement, "Maybe you weren't cut out to be a farmer (lawyer, nurse, electrician, purchasing agent, therapist, etc.)," allows people to think about how they got into a particular line of un-satisfying work. More careers are decided by chance and passing opportunity than by mature reflection, and reminding folks that most of us will have two or three or more separate careers (not jobs, *careers*) can give sufferers a sense of freedom and flexibility. As I once observed to a suicidal insurance salesman who hated himself for high-pressuring old people into buying policies they didn't need, "What's a decent fellow like you doing in a job like this?"—after which, he went into real estate.

In terms of intolerable relationships, and since half the marriages today end in divorce, the statement, "Maybe you and Shirley weren't made for each other after all," can open up the possibility that out there, somewhere in the future, some other more suitable mate awaits (right person, right place). In my own view, no marriage is worth preserving if someone has to die, or threaten to die, to keep it together.

To lock this right person, wrong place change of thinking into place, I have found it very helpful to relieve people of the weight of their own past decisions by saying, "You know, we all make the best decisions we can. We get the best information we can find at the time, and we just do it. There's no other way. But, sometimes, we don't have enough good information—including and especially about ourselves. Maybe that's what happened here. What do you think?"

Once sufferers can see that, like the rest of us who have to make choices, there will never be enough perfect information to make perfect decisions, they can stop feeling so guilty for being stupid. Making what later turn out to be mistakes is an inescapable fact of life—it's why they put erasers on pencils. Besides, a mistake is nothing more than a good decision that's aged a little.

29) *Take a Deep Breath.* Many suicidal people are under acute and chronic stress. As a result, not only their minds, but their bodies feel out of control. To help them gain a sense of mastery over these feelings of discomfort and panic, they can be quickly taught a simple breathing technique. The goal is to give them the "sigh of relief." More formal relaxation training can be used as well. Here are the in-office instructions.

- Inhale deeply and hold your breath for several seconds.

- Now exhale through your mouth, feeling the tension flow out with the air.

- Sighing may not feel comfortable at first, but it will with a little practice.

- In that moment before inhaling again, you will feel a certain stillness. This calm is called relaxation.

- Inhale again, hold it, exhale. Feel the relaxation.

- Try to take at least 40 or 50 deep breaths each day. You can do this anytime, anyplace.

- Also, whenever you find yourself in a stressful situation or you find yourself thinking about suicide, take a deep breath, hold it for a moment, and then exhale. Repeat this a few times. Then, in this moment of peace, enjoy yourself but try to think about what it was that got you to thinking about death. Jot this down and we'll talk about it at our next session.

I often have people keep a 3x5 card or note pad handy so that, after they've calmed down a bit, they can jot down what was happening to trigger their felt tension, stress, negative self-talk, and suicidal ideation. Not only does this breathing/relaxation response give patients some immediate control over what feels out of control, but we also begin to learn about the dynamics, events, interactions, and circumstances under which patients begin thinking about self-destruction.

30) *The Hope Ploy.* If the hopelessness that breeds suicide is contagious, so too is hope itself. As this social contagion concept applies to therapy, it is well to remember that long after a successful course of treatment has ended, patients often report that the single most important thing that kept them going was their therapist's faith in them. While the patient was frequently ready to give it up, the therapist never was. As perceived and remembered by the patient, it was the therapist's tenacious belief in a positive outcome that led to the ultimate victory over despair and the undoing of the forever decision.

Based on anecdotal reports, I have often heard the survivors of a suicide say, "I knew he was going to do it," or, "There was no stopping her...I finally gave up myself." These after-the-fact expressions of hopelessness seem to coincide with the suicidal person's final approach to death.

If it is not clear by now, it should be: Unyielding hope is the first, best, strongest antidote to suicide.

Throughout the course of therapy, it is important to remember you are not the one in trouble—the patient is. At this point in the history of humankind, understanding and treating suicidal people is more art than science. There is no one way to do therapy. Common elements are found in all effective therapies, but no one knows for sure how therapy "ought" to be done.

Sure, you'll make mistakes. You may even blunder once or twice. You may let a therapy session slip out of control. You may say something impossibly insensitive. Even ignorant. But that's okay. Don't worry. So long as your vision is clear and the goal of saving a life utmost in your mind, how far wrong can you go?

Patients are mostly understanding, forgiving, and tolerant. Rather than grading your performance for adequacy, they are much more likely to study your face for sincerity and some sign that you believe their lives are not as hopeless as they believe them to be. If you make a mistake and quickly own it, they'll forgive you much more readily than you may be willing to forgive yourself. So cut yourself a little slack and just do the best you can.

6 $\qquad\qquad\qquad$ ...

Special Problems

T here are, in my view, three sets of special problems in the treatment and therapy of suicidal people: the problems the patients bring to us in therapy; the problems with the treatment/therapy system; and the problems we bring to the therapy. Let me begin with the special problems of patients.

The Chronically Suicidal

Despite Nietzsche's statement that, "The thought of suicide is a great consolation; by means of it one gets successfully through many a bad night," some people can carry a good thing too far. I am speaking here of my work with several chronically suicidal people who, in the course of their therapy, taught me a great deal about suicide and how it can become a central theme of life itself.

My use of the term "chronically suicidal" is not the same as Menninger's where, in his analysis, a "chronic suicide" is someone who finds the idea of suicide repugnant, but who nevertheless chooses to die a slow death by abusing drugs or alcohol or engaging in other life- and health-threatening behavior. Rather, my term describes someone who is plagued by suicidal ideation that persists for months and years, not days and weeks. These thoughts may or may not be accompanied by gestures or attempts. Lethality of efforts to end life do not figure into my equation, although the more serious any attempt, the greater the risk. For my purposes alone, I have further divided the chronically suicidal into groups as follows:

The Suicide Dreamers

It is quite clear (to me, at any rate) that there is a subgroup of people who are constantly plagued by the wish to die but who never actually make an attempt. After a time, their suicidal thinking and dreaming seems to serve as a fantasy journey that can, oddly enough, reduce anxiety. Going to the "suicide outlet" produces a sense of calm and relaxation. As such, it is probably a conditioned response that lowers general autonomic nervous system arousal.

In such a self-hypnotic mode, thinking of suicide becomes a kind of psychic tranquilizer that, taken in small doses in times of stress and loss and conflict, can provide on-command relief from the pain of existence. Patients thus self-trained and invested in their escape from psychic suffering will not, as you might guess, be easily persuaded to simply, "give up such foolish notions." In all the cases I have treated, dreaming of suicide had become a well established cognitive escape—complete with a special setting, repetitive thoughts, melancholy themes, a mode of death, and sometimes, even mood music.

In the case of one 17-year-boy I worked with, he described in detail how he would retreat to his room after a conflicted and difficult family dinner, turn on his "suicide music," and lie in the dark with his eyes closed while he imagined slowly working a knife into his chest and heart. This quiet time was the only peace he was able to find in what he perceived to be an impossible world. By the time I saw him, he had perfected this suicide dreaming over a period of two years, during which time he had memorized all the lyrics to such songs as "Fade to Black" by Metallica and "Deep Cuts the Knife" by Helix, detailed his funeral arrangements, and imagined his parents weeping great tears of regret as he was lowered away.

Therapy With Dreamers

Good treatment for dreamers would include any of the cognitive-behavioral therapy approaches, dynamic psychotherapies, and, if appropriate, medications.

My approach to helping these suicide dreamers (some experts call them chronic ideators) is to first teach them about the functional purpose of their repetitive cognitions. Essentially, I explain how human beings learn, how we acquire habits (including unpleasant cognitive ones), and how, then, such habits can be unlearned. This is fundamental learning theory and I try to keep it simple and non-judgmental, i.e., we learn what makes us feel good. And just as bad habits can be learned, they can likewise be unlearned.

I also reassure suicide dreamers that "just because you think about suicide does not mean you have to do it." By separating thought from action, a wedge is driven between the two and tension is reduced. I also stress that people who think a lot about suicide tend not be impulsive, so it isn't likely they will suddenly jump up and kill themselves. Finally, I remind them that we human beings are free to imagine any damn thing we want to; it's what we *do* that gets us in trouble.

Sometimes a paradoxical suggestion will help free the patient from the bonds of their suicidal ideation. For example, I might say, "Just so I can get some idea about how much time you are actually spending thinking about suicide, could you take this 3x5 card and keep track of the total minutes and hours you spend doing it this week?" This direction immediately places the patient in the role of both collaborator and observer—requiring him or her to measure what has been (too often) an uncontrollable stream of consciousness.

If I get back a data base that says the patient spends an average of 40 minutes a day thinking about suicide, I might then suggest, "Hummm.... I wonder... As an experiment for the next week, I'd like you to think about suicide for at least 60 minutes each day. Nothing else now... just suicide."

As a paradoxical instruction, the patient is now obliged to take full control of his or her ideations. Being asked to exaggerate a troublesome symptom automatically puts the patient "in charge" of the very thing that is so bothersome. Whereas others might say, "Stop that, you're scaring me" or, "If you think about it too much you might just do it," this technique places the patient in control. If you are actively building in other levels of awareness, helping substitute good habits for bad, and otherwise finding new solutions to old problems, things can move quite quickly.

By acknowledging the powerful tonic their suicide dreaming provides them, I also help dreamers accept their thoughts as the normal progression of troubled persons who have been unable to come up with better solutions to life's problems. By normalizing how they came by such thoughts, and then offering substitutes for cognitive cues to relief and relaxation (why not imagine lying on a sandy beach on a faraway island instead?), I try to gentle them toward a shift from the escapist, passive pseudosolution of self-destruction to a more proactive, problem-attack approach.

The work here involves explanation, gentle confrontation, paradoxical instruction, practice sessions in cognitive retraining, and redefining problems in ways that suggest new solutions. As many suicide dreamers are extremely passive people with limited self-esteem, assertiveness training can be extremely helpful. Unaware of how to get their needs met within their limited social network, group therapy can be a life-saver.

The Suicide Actors

In my experience, most chronically suicidal people who act on their self-destructive feelings are also suicide dreamers. The difference between the two groups, as I see them, is that the suicide actors are much more socially engaged and, as a result, their suicidality has clear interpersonal consequences. For the therapist, a patient who only dreams about suicide is not nearly so anxiety producing as one who acts out those dreams.

Since people who repeatedly act on their suicidal thoughts and do not die are still with us, there is some question about how truly serious they are about ending their lives. Experts constantly advise us to take every suicide threat seriously, and this is good advice. However, for the chronic suicide actor who has made, say, 15 gestures of low lethality, some clinicians may ask, "Is this behavior better described as attention seeking?"

The answer is probably "yes." And the answer is certainly "yes" for patients who have so conditioned their minds and bodies that cutting, or burning their skin with a cigarette, or otherwise engaging in some form of self mutilation has now come to effect a sense of relief and control over, at least, their bodies.

Having written a book for the general public on suicide, I can tell you from the letters I've received that some folks clearly have defined themselves as "suicidals." One lady wrote (rather boastfully) that she had made better than 3,000 attempts on her life and, she was willing to wager, I had never met anyone so "suicidal." As I've known several people who killed themselves on their first attempt, this lady and I may not be using the term "suicidal" to mean the same thing.

However, what this lady and several other patients have taught me is that "being suicidal" can take on all the rights and obligations required of any other social identity. People who constantly employ suicidal threats, gestures, and non-lethal attempts over a period of months and years do, by their actions, become known for this clearly definable form of interpersonal communication.

If I may speculate for a moment, it is not difficult to see how someone might become a chronic suicide actor. Announcing you are now suicidal causes several rather immediate interpersonal effects in our society:

- People stop what they are doing and pay attention.
- People who have been mistreating you stop mistreating you—at least in the short term.
- People who are threatening to leave you stop threatening to leave you (you can't leave a dying person).
- People who are about to fire you, give you an F, expel you from school, or take other sanctions against you may reconsider.

- Doctors, clergymen, therapists, counselors, and others who give aid and assistance to those in need can be convinced to give even more aid and assistance.

On a larger scale, our society has taken the position that, if we know you are about to end your own life, we will do everything humanly possible to stop you. For the chronic suicide actor, this means a safe harbor can always be found—provided, of course, a rescue signal is sent in the clear and the people on the receiving end are awake and alert.

Chronic suicide actors know the drill. Given their considerable experience with how people respond to suicidal threats and gestures, they have learned very well how to find respite from an emotional storm, or a difficult family situation, or a fight with a roommate, or even the unpleasant restrictiveness of a county jail. Five simple words can generally get those in power to take some action: "I want to kill myself."

No matter how you slice it, suicidal people wield a lot of power. And so they should. But when you are dealing with someone who has come to cope with all of life's struggles by playing the trump card ("I'm willing to die to get my way on this"), you now have a very special therapy problem.

Therapy For Actors

Therapy for suicide actors is much riskier. And because of the risks, it's scarier. Basic good treatment would include both individual and group therapy by therapists well trained in how to work with personality disorders. On the cognitive side, the approach to the chronic suicide actor is not much different than that you would take with a chronic dreamer— except that the following items should be kept in mind:

- Acting on suicidal ideas is quantitatively different than just thinking about them, and the risk of death much higher. Sometimes suicide actors die when they didn't intend to; for example, the people who were supposed to get the rescue call about their overdose were dozing.

- Actors have clearly defined to others that they are prepared to die, or at least hurt themselves. Having been witnessed in the act of self-destruction, they have clearly, if unconsciously, asked others to confirm them in this powerful role. Therefore, their investment is higher in any possible outcome and they are much more prepared than dreamers to act out.

- No one would ever want to grow up to be known as, say, "Kid Suicide." This social identity is not something the person wanted, but rather got tagged with after making one or more threats, gestures, or attempts.

- However else they may be perceived, such people are almost always severely damaged folks. In my experience, most are abuse victims of tragic proportion. Despite their sutures, scars, and overdoses, suicide actors want the same things the rest of us want: a little love, sharing, understanding, and acceptance.

- Suicide actors know a lot more about what it takes to *not* kill a human being than you can ever guess. I've known suicide actors who kept a Physicians' Desk Reference by their bedside to measure just how large a just-sublethal dose of pills should be. Or who knew which way to slice the wrists to get a maximum of blood and minimum of damage to nerves and tendons. For the chronic suicide actor, and in terms of mastery and control, committing suicide has become a highly developed skill. In fact, several patients I've worked with refer to their attempts as completions, as in, "The first time I committed suicide was in 1974. The next time was 1981. And then...."

- As an answer to the ancient and existential question, "Who am I?," being suicidal is certainly one answer. Helping someone alter this definition of self ("I'm the man who kills himself") will necessarily require challenging not only the self-statements that make such acting possible, but the social perceptions of others as well.

Basically, helping suicide actors change who they are and how others see them may be the only way to protect such people from being obliged to live *down* to the expectations others now have of them. If you think in terms of process, you can imagine how, after several months of threats, gestures, and sublethal attempts, the sense of initial alarm passes in observers and, too often, becomes one of indifference, or even anger. As a son once said to a father who had been talking about suicide for several months, "Dad, I'm real tired of listening to this... why don't you just go ahead and get it over with." His father obliged the same day. It should be obvious that therapy for the entire family or system of significant others is always indicated for actors.

I should quickly add here that, at least in my experience, the patient's significant others are not always very interested in learning to deal with a healthier person. After all, they've come to know and love old "Suicide Sally" and may not be at all pleased that some therapist is trying to help her with a make-over. One roommate of a chronically suicidal patient I was seeing (and who'd come into a session) remarked, "At least when she was suicidal, I knew what to expect."

To help chronic suicide actors, therapists simply must get right in the middle of these social perceptions and negative-outcome expectations, challenge them, and help everyone come to a fresh understanding.

Of all the so-called personality disorders that display this chronic suicide actor behavior, the borderline personality is clearly the most difficult to work with. For these patients, their early careers in suicidality have led them into emergency rooms, psychiatric inpatient settings, outpatient counseling, or mental health programs where, after working their way into the hearts and minds of dozens of treatment staff, they have become extremely adept at playing the suicide card. Given their developmental histories of abuse, neglect, abandonment, and the building up of approximately one million dollars in psychological debts against humanity, you can't really blame these people for trying to get a little extra attention.

But they shouldn't have to kill themselves to get it.

The good news about borderline patients is, by the way, that if they can meet a therapist or program staff who understands them well enough to set and keep decent limits and boundaries, most will eventually get better, grow up, and one day give up their madcap careers in suicide. Based on studies and the personal experience of therapists, borderline patients show much improvement over the course of good treatment—so much so that, some years down the road, they will no longer warrant the diagnosis. Unfortunately, a higher than expected rate of borderline patients kill themselves.

Dealing With An E.R.A.

A really well thought out suicide plan can be, in the eyes of a chronically suicidal person, a thing of beauty. Both dreamers and actors may have such plans. And, in the same way an Individual Retirement Account ensures a safe financial passage to old age, an E.R.A. (Early Retirement Account, a.k.a. suicide plan) assures the suicidal person control over the end of his or her life.

For the suicidal person, the Early Retirement Account may be a couple of bottles of sleeping pills, a gun and a special bullet, a length of garden hose, grandfather's old straight razor or, in more recent times, a copy of the Derek Humphry *Final Exit* book and the recommended amount of over-the-counter medication.

Sometimes the E.R.A. represents a lifetime of thinking and planning. Sometimes the E.R.A. is a major and recent investment—for example, the purchase of an expensive .44 magnum handgun. But whatever it is, the seriously suicidal person is not likely to just hand it over to you because you asked for it.

No way. Psychologically speaking, he or she is going to arm wrestle you for it. Not once, but possibly every single time you meet for a therapy session. In fact, sometimes the entire focus and goal of a long psychotherapeutic struggle is to get the person to give up, finally and forever, the Early Retirement Account.

And that's okay. So long as you don't lose the faith, things can and do work out.

System Problems

A second source of special problems faced by suicidal people entering treatment are those posed by the system of care itself. And while this little text is not the place to address how mental health care is delivered in our society, allow me to share with you what I consider to be several additional risks taken by anyone who comes to us for help.

- The person you first told your story to is not the person who will work with you. As a continuity of care issue, many suicidal patients complain that they have to tell upwards of a half a dozen people their story before someone agrees to be their therapist.

- What's wrong with you, this agency doesn't treat. If your underlying problem is alcoholism, the mental health intake worker you just told your story to now wants to (must?) refer you to an appropriate alcohol treatment facility.

- Or, if you are being admitted to an alcohol treatment facility and mention that you've been suicidal, the intake worker you've just told your story to will (must?) now refer you to a mental health facility.

- The therapist you have finally come to know and trust is leaving the agency, or taking a different job, or going back to school, or transferring you to another program.

Therapy is hard enough. But being transferred about like a piece of lost luggage in a bus station is impossible for people with major attachment and abandonment issues and fears. Anytime there is a transfer of a suicidal patient from one therapist to another, considerable risk accrues to the patient. Although often unavoidable, all such transfers need to be handled with kid gloves and carefully discussed with the patient well in advance.

Note: The loss of a therapist can sometimes be nothing if not catastrophic. If I could rule the world, I would make it a felony to transfer any suicidal patient except for the most unavoidable of reasons.

- The therapist you see doesn't really give a damn whether you live or die. Mental health systems are not without people whose milk of human kindness soured long ago. When such people are, somehow, put in positions of responsibility vis-a-vis the intervention and treatment of suicidal patients, nothing good can come of it. Should you know of such a person (hostile, cold, angry, and mean tempered toward suicidal people in particular), please take it upon yourself to get that person out of the field—or at least promoted to a safe distance from any suicide sufferer.

Obviously there are other system problems, but these are the most serious ones. Simple availability of treatment services is probably the largest single roadblock to low- and medium-income people at risk for suicide. However, the fact of being suicidal has become one of the sure ways to get an appointment in even the most overtaxed community mental health center.

Our Problems

The problems we therapists bring to suicidal patients are probably as broad as they are deep. As I've already covered what I consider to be some of the major issues one must consider before doing this work, here I will simply outline some additional notions for therapists who are already doing it.

First, I don't know if it is even possible *not* to develop strong feelings toward suicidal patients. There is something fundamentally crazy about spending a good portion of any day on this wonderful little planet trying to talk people out of leaving it sooner than they have to. Or, as an old purchasing agent fishing pal often says, "How in the hell do you do that all day long?" Which leads me to the first rule for heading off the problems we bring to the suicidal patient.

Rule 1. If at all possible, limit the number of actively suicidal patients you work with. People who have passed through their suicide crisis and are on the mend don't keep you up at night, but people teetering on the edge are another matter. In sum, don't overindulge in this exciting work.

Rule 2. Share every case. No life or death call should be made by one person. Consults help. Spending time with supervisors is critical. Even a formal debriefing after a tough session or difficult triage decision is essential to maintaining a sense of well being.

Rule 3. Monitor your feelings toward suicidal patients. Fully expect to develop strong emotions both during and after sessions. Many therapists feel themselves retreat during sessions, slip into daydreaming, or otherwise step out of the emotional swirl brought on by acutely distressed patients. This is okay; just know it's happening.

Rule 4. Keep your balance about who has the problem. Many suicidal patients will try to convince you *their* life is in *your* hands. And while you have already made up your mind that no suicidal patient will die with your approval, it is also the case that, in the final analysis, each of us (suicidal or not) is ultimately responsible for what happens to us.

Rule 5. Recognize your own need to deny a suicidal patient's communications of a wish to die. A suicide threat made to a therapist is often a threat to our sense of competence. If an at-risk patient dies by suicide while in our care, won't our friends and colleagues wonder if we are really competent? Sufficiently trained? Or maybe we were even unprofessional?

Rule 6. Do not let a patient put you in the role of savior. If you become the only person in the world who can save the suicidal person from him- or herself, you are automatically increasing the risk to both of you. Becoming idealized is one step from being worshiped; being worshiped is one step from falling from grace.

Rule 7. The instant you feel yourself becoming bored with a suicidal patient, find a panic button to hit. Discuss this feeling with a supervisor or colleague. This feeling may show up as a passing thought that maybe this patient would do better in group or could be transferred to a new student therapist.

Rule 8. The instant you feel any anger toward a suicidal patient, find two panic buttons to push. Feeling anger toward a patient you once got along with, and even liked, is proof positive that something is going wrong with the therapy. Supervision is strongly indicated.

Rule 9. If you begin to feel inadequate, anxious, are late for an appointment and/or catch yourself wishing you had gone into another field of endeavor as you prepare to meet with a suicidal patient, again, get some help from your friends.

Rule 10. Examine if, in fact, you are managing your suicidal patients the same as your other patients. Do you accept appointments at all hours for these patient? Three a.m. phone calls? Have you agreed to call them once a day to see if they are safe?

Since they won't let you into this field without a fairly high score on some co-dependency scale or other, do suicidal patients take you out of your usual sense of balance and control about how to help others? If so, some introspection and outside help may keep you on the beam.

As I see it, it is our job to invest the time, energy, and attention to self necessary to do this work well. And this work, in my view, cannot be done well without managing our countertransference feelings. To do it well we must lead, help, assist, and sometimes push troubled patients into exactly those strong emotions, painful memories, and sources of conflict that have brought them to the brink of self-destruction. Doing anything less may not be enough.

The able therapist for a suicidal patient is someone who has a good sense of self, an articulated philosophy of life, and also the courage to take the patient on what often proves a frightful journey—for both of them.

This is how therapy should be. Always aware that the patient may die along the way, we must accept this possibility, keep an eye on it, but push ahead into the darkest corners of existence where, as it turns out, the real work of therapy takes place. Then, when our day is done, we need to take especially good care of ourselves, be kind to our friends and lovers, and remember to enjoy our milk and cookies.

Special Topics

• • •

In this section you will find a variety of topics of potential interest. As some patients or situations may present with more problems than others, the plan here is to give you as much condensed information as space allows with the least possible expenditure of time on your part.

Because suicide is always multi-determined, it is helpful to know at least a little about all the known variables that may play a part in any given situation, or with any given individual. Therefore, by selecting relevant topic areas, you can quickly access bits and sources of information that should prove useful to your work.

For example, if your client is going through a divorce, abusing alcohol and depressed, the sections on Divorce, Alcohol, and Depression should prove helpful. If you are a school counselor and your school has had a suicide, the sections on Contagion, Postvention, and Survivors will give you a starting place and a possible plan of action. Highly condensed, these facts, procedures, and suggestions for action have been extracted from both personal experiences and the source materials listed under References and Readings.

Adolescents

From a September 1991 *Los Angeles Times* feature, here's a headline to give us all the willies: "A million teenagers attempt suicide in a year." Of these, 276,000 suffered injuries serious enough to require medical attention. The stuff of national news, the very idea of young people thinking about killing themselves unnerves us all.

However you juggle the numbers from the Centers for Disease Control (the people who keep the statistics), there is little doubt now that the rate of teen suicide has at least tripled (some say quadrupled) in the last 30 years.

However frightening these figures are, here's something to keep in mind: Since 1977 the rate of completed suicides among young people has leveled off and now matches the overall rate for individuals of all ages (about 12 per 100,000). The incidents for suicidal behavior (thoughts, threats, gestures, and attempts), however, seem epidemic.

Those Most at Risk

Beginning with longstanding problems from childhood, a troubled youth enters adolescence only to face even more daunting developmental tasks and challenges: increased sexual feelings, finding and making same-aged friends, succeeding in competitive education, and coping with increasing estrangement from parents while transitioning into adulthood. Without proven interpersonal skills, little history of success in meeting life's demands, and no work experience to fall back on for self-esteem, a great many youths enter a window of vulnerability to suicidal behavior.

In the final stages of an adolescent suicide crisis there is often a rapid breakdown in existing relationships, sudden changes in behavior, and typically some display of verbal or behavioral threats and/or gestures.

Here are some of the best data available to describe the psychological and social problems of suicidal young people (from Teicher, 1979):

- Twenty percent had a parent who attempted suicide.
- Forty percent had a parent, relative, or close friend who attempted suicide.
- Seventy-two percent had one or both natural parents absent from the home, divorced, separated, or deceased.
- Eighty-four percent who had a stepparent felt severe conflict with the stepparent and alienation from the family.
- Fifty-eight percent had a parent who had been married more than once.
- Sixty-two percent had both parents working, or in one-parent families, that parent worked.
- The adolescents had undergone serious environmental changes—among others, parental remarriage, hospitalization of family members, death in the family, change of school, being sent to foster care, or being placed in juvenile detention.
- In 16 percent of suicide attempts, parental alcoholism had caused serious interpersonal problems.
- Large numbers lived without care from parents, in foster families, or with relations.
- Families had marked residential mobility that made enduring ties to peers, teachers, and other family members impossible.

Acute Stressors

As a background note, the National Institute of Mental Health reports some 12 percent of all youths suffer from severe mental illness. Almost 3 in 10 will have an alcohol problem. Coupled with a backdrop of psychosocial conflict just listed, here is a partial list of the acute stressors which typically precipitate an *acute* suicidal crisis. In no order of importance, they are:

- Divorce of parents
- A major family move resulting in separation from peers.
- Death of someone in the family, a friend, or someone in school, especially by suicide.
- Loss of a boy- or girlfriend. In many cases, this attachment is the only one the child has. The loss can be both overwhelming and unendurable.
- The diagnosis or onset of a serious illness.
- Any disfiguring operation, injury, or accident that results in a significant negative change in body image.
- Being arrested for any crime.

Thoughts on Helping Teens

Here are a few things to keep in mind when working with teens:

- Having been one yourself, try to remember how perfectly awful being a teenager can be. This "remembering back" will carry you far in the empathy department.
- Intent to die with teenagers is sometimes difficult to determine. A boy about to lose his girlfriend may say, "If I don't get her back by Saturday, I'll kill myself."

And in the next breath say, "Then next week, I'll try something else." Careful evaluation of today's actions against the distant future is not a long suit among adolescents. The trouble is, too many teens kill themselves before they *think through the consequences.* Helping them do this thinking is our job.

• Studies clearly indicate that ordinary, garden variety depression is rampant among teens. It may be more difficult to diagnose in teens (especially in boys), but it is there all the same. And, as a reason for hope, it is highly treatable.

• Keep in mind that the kid who is acting out, angry, nasty, smoking where he shouldn't, and generally insufferable is at just as much risk of suicide as the quiet and depressed one. The "bad me!" cry for help is every bit as urgent as the "sad me" cry. Boys, by the way, specialize in this way of saying, "Hey! Somebody! I'm suckin' pond water over here! Can't anybody see!?" If you listen for the pain behind the anger, you'll hear it.

• If you work with teens, then you already know how rarely they self-refer. Most teens would rather (sometimes literally) die before asking an adult for help. Lesson: *We must go to them.* My suggestion is to reach out to a troubled teen *for any reason that has put worry in our mind.* A thin excuse is good enough. The worst a child can do if you insult him or her by suggesting a need for help is tell you to butt out. Big deal.

• Much of the suicidal behavior of teens is parasuicidal in nature and not highly lethal, especially with girls. But this doesn't mean a kid isn't in trouble and doesn't need help. Minimizing youthful threats and gestures may make us feel better, but it doesn't get at what is troubling our young people.

If you'll remember your own teen years, psychological suffering was especially poignant. Everything hurt more. Depending on your love life (or lack of a love life), you could have upwards of a couple of major tragedies a week. A lot of teens have yet to hit their first home run in life, let alone make their first relationship work. And relationships for teens are everything.

Maybe the main thing to keep in mind with teenagers is that they suffer just like the rest of us and for the same reasons we do. Like us, they have problems associated with alcohol and drug abuse; they live in angry, frightening families where there is emotional and/or physical abuse; and they suffer broken relationships and shattered dreams just like adults. The difference is, they have neither the experience nor the perspective to reflect on and cope with such life stresses—which may be why a lot of us remember our teenage years not as a phase, but as a disease.

Suicidogenic Parents

Many teens see the world as impossibly competitive, openly hostile to them (who really likes teenagers?), and sometimes peopled by adults who have said, "This family would be better off without you."

A few parents openly wish their children were dead. Many more keep such wishes to themselves but express the desire indirectly. A few parents have even suggested suicide to their children; if not in so many words, then in deeds (e.g., giving a problem boy a gun for his birthday).

Kids are especially smart about relationships and can sense across a crowded room when they're not wanted. Sometimes they're wrong in their impression gathering, but sometimes they're right. If we're working with youth, we can't afford to take chances by always believing the parents' version of reality.

At least in my view, parents who hate their children can kill them; suicide just shifts the blame to the victim. No child should die for lack of love, so this is another one of those times we need to be bold, take off our blinders (e.g., all parents love their children), and really get inside the skin and skull of the kid we're trying to help stay alive.

As a final note, let me just add that the size and shape and severity of a child's problem is always defined by the child, not by a casual observer like you or me. Or any adult for that matter. If a 17-year-old boy is arrested while driving his father's car without his permission, just got a C- on his report card, and was dumped by his girlfriend of three weeks (the girl of his dreams and the mother of his children), it doesn't mean his pain isn't worth killing himself to escape. A "tsk, tsk, young man, things will get better" is just not a sufficient response to a lad who, because of *his* perception of these tragedies, now says he wants to die. Too many young people have died trying to convince older people their pain was real.

Aggressive Behavior

As a general sign, symptom, or signal of a pending suicidal act, aggressive behavior should never be discounted as evidence a person is *not*, therefore, suicidal. Anger frequently precedes suicide. Violence, as the behavioral manifestation of anger, should always alert us to increased risk.

According to suicide researchers Joseph Teicher and Jerry Jacobs, aggression-type warning signs associated with adolescent suicide include the following: withdrawal and rebelliousness; theft and/or vandalism; unruliness in school; and bitter arguments with teachers, friends, siblings, or parents. Aggressive behavior in adults, especially toward loved ones, is also an indication of increased risk.

Basically, any sudden uncharacteristic or unusual display of anger or hostility warrants a direct question about suicidality. At the bottom of any severe relationship conflict there is often a great well of resentment and, coupled with the fear of being abandoned, such fear-driven anger can be terrible indeed. It is well to remember that about four percent of all adult suicides involve a homicide as well.

AIDS/HIV

Many people assume that those who become infected with HIV and/or develop AIDS are made, by the diagnosis alone, more suicidal. According to Stephen Platt, a researcher in the MRC Medical Sociology Unit in Glasgow, Scotland and World Health Organization consultant, too few decent studies exist to warrant leaping to this conclusion. Therefore, at least based on Platt's survey of the relationship of suicidality to HIV/AIDS, it would be a mistake to automatically assign a higher risk rating to someone just because he or she had contracted this illness.

Still, there is little doubt that receiving a positive HIV diagnosis may, sooner or later, lead to other, quite negative psychological consequences: depression, social isolation, unwanted dependency on others, economic difficulties, and so on. As these factors have traditionally been associated with higher risk of suicide, assessment and treatment for suicidality is always indicated.

In one study by Stephen G. Schneider and his co-workers at the University of California at Los Angeles, the researchers found that suicidal thoughts among some homosexual men infected with HIV reflected a coping strategy *not* associated with hopelessness, emotional distress, and depression. Their ongoing research suggests that suicidal ideation may be a way to gain a kind of mental mastery over the uncontrollable threat posed by AIDS in those infected. However, the study group did not include those whose immune systems failed and where AIDS had developed.

As with any terminal illness, maybe the most important thing to remember is that there can be no illness without an attitude *toward that illness*. People who tend to withdraw from life when struck by calamity will tend to withdraw upon learning they are HIV positive. Those who become depressed when stressed will become depressed under the stress of contracting this illness. Those who have toyed with suicide as a solution to a problem before they tested positive will doubtless toy with it again. Therefore, the best medicine is to examine these patients' histories, learn how they have coped (or not coped) in the past, and work with them to cope better in the future—no matter how foreshortened that future may be.

Alcohol

Alcohol aids and abets suicide in several ways. And while the role of alcohol abuse in suicide would take a book, here are some selected facts regarding chronic alcoholics from a review by Murphy and Wetzel:

• Alcoholism is implicated in about 25% of all U.S. suicides.

• Most alcoholics who will die by suicide do it between ages 40 and 59.

• The lifetime risk of dying by suicide if you've been hospitalized for alcoholism is 3.4%, or about 166 times greater than for non-psychiatrically ill persons.

Here's the point: Chronic alcoholics are at significant risk of suicide, especially during episodes of depression following detoxification and/or hospitalization. If I could, I would make it a law that inpatient treatment facilities be required to follow up all at-risk patients for a period of at least three months to make sure they are not experiencing suicidal feelings, thoughts, or impulses.

Recovery is tough, especially in the first few weeks and months. Unpleasant memories from pre-drinking days are suddenly activated. Losses are realized. Psychological pain often sweeps over the recovering person in great waves. Relapse is common. And, to the degree a relapse is perceived as yet another failure, the idea of killing oneself can become very appealing. It is during the first few months of sobriety that recovering people learn that getting sober is only the first step; all the real work still lies ahead.

Twenty years in substance abuse work has taught me that alcoholics pass through several windows of severe risk: when they first realize their drinking has cost them their most treasured things (job, spouse, kids, prestige, etc.); when they are a few days sober and, suddenly, an acute depressive reality sets in; and when, for whatever seemed like a good and sufficient reason, they take that first drink and relapse— thus failing *one more time*.

What too many people in the substance abuse and mental health fields fail to realize is that the majority of alcoholics (whether sober, just detoxed, or several weeks into sobriety) are clinically depressed. These symptoms will show up on the Beck Depression Inventory, or you can just run down the symptom list in an interview. You'll find plenty. And now that you know this, you have to treat the depression. Because if you don't treat the depression, you won't touch the hopelessness directly and, if you don't go after the hopelessness, you won't reduce the risk of suicide.

As I've outlined in the therapy section, there are many good reasons why you must get the alcohol out of the patient to do any decent therapy. But here are a few other points you might make with your recovering alcoholic patient to reinforce, nurture, and otherwise reward him or her for having given up the sauce:

Just stopping drinking will:

- Reduce guilt (about drinking).
- Reduce the risk of an accidental death (e.g., while driving).
- Reduce the risk of an impulsive suicide attempt.
- Improve the quality of thinking and creative problem solving.
- Make therapy and healing possible.
- Make them smarter. (Intelligence test scores improve with sobriety.)
- Permit a good night's sleep. (Restoration of sleep cycles is essential to establishing a decent mood and a growing sense of well-being.)
- Sweeten their breath, thus making social contacts possible again. (I'm only half kidding.)

Last, while chronic alcoholics are at a very high risk of eventually dying by suicide, hundreds and hundreds of non-alcoholics kill themselves every year *while under the influence*. Some studies suggest that as many as 70% of single car fatal accidents where the driver was intoxicated may be disguised suicides. Other studies indicate many suicidal, non-alcoholic people drink before and during their suicide attempts—often ingesting other drugs while they imbibe. Still others use alcohol to "get up the courage" to kill themselves by more direct means, e.g., shooting or hanging or jumping.

Ambivalence

To understand suicidal people, you need to understand the concept of ambivalence. An old psychology joke explains ambivalence thus: It's the feeling you get when you see your mother-in-law plunge over a cliff in your new Cadillac.

Basically, ambivalence is the experience of two strong feelings at the same time—one positive and one negative. In suicidal people, this amounts to experiencing the simultaneous wish to die and the wish to live. This is the rule in suicidal people, not the exception.

It is this push-pull, intense feeling of wanting to die and wanting to live that leads suicidal people to communicate their psychic struggle to the rest of us. Those who have completely resolved their ambivalence in favor of death do not communicate this struggle; they're already dead.

Therefore, the suicidal person you're working with is more like you and me than like those who've already resolved their ambivalence. No matter how suicidal a person may be, the issue at bar has not yet been settled. Only death settles all accounts. And, since you and I and everyone who is suicidal today are all still in this life together, we still have a chance. Helping suicidal people understand that ambivalence is the norm for people in crisis can, by itself, help them postpone the forever decision and survive.

American Association Of Suicidology (AAS)

If you or your agency or school or hospital are going to be working with suicidal folks, this is a good outfit to join. A non-profit organization founded in 1968, its goals are to understand and prevent suicide, support survivors, encourage research, certify crisis intervention programs, assist the media with scientifically sound information, and otherwise work on a regional and national level toward better understanding of suicide and what can be done to prevent it across the life cycle. It has several extremely useful publications, including the journal, *Suicide and Life-Threatening Behavior,* and *Newslink*, a quarterly newsletter. Central office address and phone: AAS, 2459 S. Ash Street, Denver, CO 80222; phone: (303) 692-0985.

Anniversary Phenomenon

All of us with memories are blessed (or cursed) with the so-called anniversary phenomenon. Because we have memories, we can recall past events that, right or wrong, can have a powerful influence on our present moods, thoughts, and actions. Sometimes, for the suicidal person, the anniversary of some loss or some special source of sadness can trigger thoughts of suicide. Not uncommonly, the anniversary of the death by suicide of a parent or best friend or sibling can, because of our human ability to empathize and associate our feelings with those of others, precipitate a suicidal crisis in someone who is vulnerable.

Because all depressed people are, at least statistically, suicide receptive (i.e., open to the idea of suicide as a way to exit that black hole into which they toss depressed folks), it is always a good idea to take a careful history of major losses and the dates these occurred.

Deaths of children, parents, and especially any suicides by loved ones need to be explored for their continuing effect on the patient. Once you know these anniversary dates, you can confirm with the patient that, yes, "the holidays are an especially sad season for me because my father killed himself the day after Christmas," and you can stay on top of things and provide a little something extra in the caring department during these recurrent episodes of renewed grief.

Note: Despite protestations to the contrary and all sorts of sophisticated denials, the death of a parent by suicide is *never* insignificant in the psychological makeup of a child. Or an adolescent. Or an adult survivor. Knowing this history and working it through is essential to good intervention and treatment.

Antidepressants

Antidepressants are one of the miracles of modern psychiatry. They go by many names and while not perfect solutions to every depression, their medicinal effect on a clinically depressed mood can be nothing if not amazing. As a psychiatrist friend of mine jokes, "This lady isn't depressed, she's Prozac deficient."

Antidepressants don't work well for everyone, but they work for most. Based on a major and ongoing depression research project conducted by the National Institute of Mental Health, pharmacotherapy alone (antidepressants) results in alleviation of depressive symptoms in 57% of the cases. Interpersonal psychotherapy and cognitive-behavioral therapies are very nearly as effective as the antidepressants and, while all the data are not in, talk therapy *and* antidepressants may be the most beneficial over the long haul.

Non-addicting, antidepressants pack enough punch that they should not be given in large dosages to actively suicidal people, lest they overdose on them before they begin to positively impact depressive symptoms. In terms of lifting depressed moods, antidepressants can be counted on to do their work in about 10 to 14 days—depending on the specific drug, the patient, the absorption rate, blood levels achieved, and so forth. The main message for those of us who cannot prescribe medications is that we need to support their use when clinically indicated—if for no other reason than to give patients a reason to hope for an end to their misery.

Interestingly, some depressed, suicidal people don't want to take pills because taking them could mean they've decided to go on living. For example, if they haven't yet decided to live, they may accept a prescription but not fill it. Or take the medication home from the drugstore but never open it. Medications are sometimes seen as a sign of failure in our fiercely independent culture; a teenaged boy once told me, "If I start taking pills now, I'll never stop."

This kind of resistance aside, medications are especially indicated where there have been prior episodes of depression and/or a history of either alcoholism or mood disorders in the family, or where the depression seems entrenched, chronic, and has not given way to supportive counseling or any sort of individual or group psychotherapy.

As the final word on exactly what causes depressions is not in (Traumatic life events? Losses? An imbalance in brain chemistry? Crooked chromosomes? Too few green vegetables? Prozac deficiency? etc.), the main order of business for those of us in the life saving business is not to worry so much about how depressions start, as how to end them. Until the mysteries of the blues are better understood, and for the sake of our suicidal patients, no proven remedy should be overlooked.

Note: While it helps to work with a psychiatrist around issues of antidepressants and other psychotropic medications, other physicians prescribe these drugs all the time. The trick is to work together closely with your MD, because when it comes to suicidal people, the more professionals on the team, the better.

Assessment

Assessment is simply the process by which data are gathered to form an opinion about the size, shape, and seriousness of some problem or other; in our case, someone's risk of taking his or her own life. Assessment includes collecting interview data, observations made by yourself and others and, most importantly, the thoughts, feelings, impulses, and internal observations of self and circumstance made by the suicidal person.

Assessment can include the use of questionnaires, scales, psychological tests, demographic facts, and other such sources of information as will help us understand the relative risk a given person might be at—*on that day.*

Because suicidality is a dynamic process, the factors that influence the decision to act on a wish to die are seldom predictable and, therefore, preventive action is not always possible. The lesson, then, is that we must assess suicidality in suicidal people *all the time.* Or at least until we're convinced the crisis has passed.

Having reviewed many suicides by active patients in mental health and substance abuse treatment programs, I can assure you that one assessment for suicide risk at the beginning of treatment is not enough. A vulnerable person can go along for years mildly depressed and passively receptive to the idea of suicide and then, boom! Something dreadful and unplanned happens. An unanticipated bit of bad news, a frightening medical diagnosis, the unexpected loss of a love, or some other "last straw" is added to the burden of living. Suddenly the scales tip toward death and, before the counselor ever has a chance to intervene and do something positive, the person suicides.

While it is well to remember that while many people are vulnerable to suicide by reason of a stack of risk factors (age, race, suicidal family history, alcoholism, etc.), it is the precipitating events, the "last straws" that are so hard to anticipate, understand, and put into a formula that would lead to better prediction of suicidality. Therefore, it is my recommendation that brief, but ongoing, assessment be a part of any treatment plan.

This assessment need not be complicated. A few simple questions should do it. With particularly vulnerable or chronically suicidal, high-risk clients, I try never to let a session pass but that I inquire, "How are we doing? Any suicidal thoughts or feelings this week?"

Attempted Suicide

There is some debate about just what this term means, but most experts define an attempt as an effort to die that, *had the person not been stopped or saved,* would have resulted in death. As compared to a gesture, which is more symbolic and less lethal, an attempt often results in serious medical consequences: deep lacerations requiring sutures, life-saving heroics by paramedics or emergency room personnel, stomach pumping, and so on. Generally, the person who makes an attempt has formed the conscious intent to die, and, therefore, the risk of eventual suicide is much higher.

Autoerotic Asphxiation

Autoerotic asphyxiation is a method of partial self-strangulation that, effected during sexual arousal and masturbation by increasing constriction of the air passage, can heighten the pleasure associated with orgasm. At least some deaths ruled suicide by hanging are, in fact, caused by this non-death seeking activity. Almost entirely a phenomenon found in young men, the behavior is more associated with poor judgment, not suicidal intent. Unfortunately, should a coroner rule the death a suicide, survivors may suffer unnecessary guilt and self-recrimination over a wrong conclusion.

Clues To Suicide (Forms Of Communication)

A great deal has been written about the so-called "clues to suicide." Generally such listings of clues include direct verbal clues, indirect verbal clues, and behavioral clues.

- Verbal clues include such things as frank statements of intent, e.g., "I'm going to kill myself," or, "I'm going to end it all."

- Indirect verbal clues communicate the same information, but with less clarity. Sometimes coded and requiring deciphering, some examples might be: "What's the point in living? I can't go on anymore," or, "Everyone would be better off without me," or, "Here, take my guitar, I won't be needing it after Friday."

- Behavioral clues are simply acts or actions that suggest a person is making final arrangements in anticipation of death by suicide: making a will, buying a gun, arranging final affairs, making funeral plans, giving away money or prized possessions, and so forth. For many young people, an abnormal concern or preoccupation with death in drawings or writings may signal suicidal fantasies.

Here are some useful ways to think about clues as forms of communication.

- One clue does not a suicidal person make. Sending or leaving several clues is the rule, not the exception. The better part of valor is *never take any clue lightly* and, if in doubt, ask.

- All clues (verbal, coded, behavioral) are a form of interpersonal communication. However poorly a vague hint like, "I just want out of this mess," might be, the encoded message is, "Hey! I'm in real trouble over here!"

- Suicide gestures and attempts are, without a single word being spoken, clear forms of communication. The man whose wife is about to leave him and who then, in a desperate act, takes a non-lethal dose of barbiturates is saying, in effect, "Can't you see I can't live without you?" Therefore, a suicide gesture or attempt is often clear and convincing evidence of the failure of mere language to solve problems between people.

- It is important to remember that non-verbal, behavioral clues are every bit as important as verbal ones. The body language of folding one's arm to lock out others, hateful stares, and missing a scheduled therapy appointment are all potentially powerful clues to some breakdown in communication.

• Suicide clues are not sent at random; they are sent to other people—almost always to the most important people in that person's life. As such, they are usually part of some ongoing (and failing) dialogue between the people involved. Find out who is not correctly interpreting messages being sent and, from a therapeutic angle, you should be halfway home.

In this last regard, maybe the most important thing to remember about so-called clues to suicide is that, for whatever reason the sufferer is not getting through to those he or she needs to, he or she is *not getting through*. There are some fairly obvious reasons for this, all of which may prove fatal.

For example, the one the suicidal person has been trying to signal might be too frightened to acknowledge the reality that someone—an acquaintance, friend, lover, relative— wants to die. Or, depending on how much trouble a relationship is in, the receiver of the communiqué would just as soon the suicidal person stop hinting and get it over with. Silence, turning away, changing the subject and/or a non-response is often typical in such lethal setups.

I have even seen cases in which the person who was being sent messages of suicidal intent figured it was "good medicine" to simply ignore people who talk about killing themselves. I have also seen cases where the person being sent a pile of suicide clues is too angry to "hear" anything. Clearly, in cases like these, the interventionist and/or therapist must focus on the failing communications network, not just the suicidal person.

Last, not everyone will send or leave clues suggesting they are planning to take their lives. Among suicidologists, there is a general agreement that somewhere between 5 and 10 or even 20 percent of all suicides do not communicate their intentions to anyone. But since it is impossible to interview the deceased, there is no way to tell if this is true. In fact, many of the things we really need to know about the people who actually kill themselves are irretrievably lost at the moment of death.

Confidentiality

Professionally-assured confidentiality is the direct descendant of our constitutionally guaranteed right to privacy. As the concept has been inherited by therapists, doctors, lawyers, institutions in general, and those in the healing professions in particular, confidentiality remains much misunderstood. Confidential information gathered from a troubled person is not ours; it belongs to the troubled person. He or she decides who gets to see or hear about anything deemed sensitive or even, for example, the fact that a conversation between us took place.

Despite this right to privacy, however, the present courts have held that it is not okay to kill yourself and, therefore, the rules of confidentiality do not hold for people so inclined. What this means is that, if you have made a good faith determination that the person you are dealing with is at high risk of suicide and potentially dangerous to him- or herself, you can do what any reasonably prudent individual would do under similar circumstances: notify family, call the police, contact a mental health authority for an evaluation, insist on a second opinion, etc. And while it would be nice to have the suicidal person's consent, *it is not necessary*.

Yes, you may risk damaging a therapeutic alliance, incurring a lawsuit, or be on the receiving end of some immediate, but generally short-lived wrath, but it is unlikely you will be found guilty of violating someone's right to privacy for having sought help to save a life. I've personally dealt with any number of people whose confidentiality was breached during a suicidal crisis and, no matter how angry they might have been in the beginning, every one of them later understood why it had to be done. (More of this in the section dealing with risk management.)

Contagion/Cluster

This section of material is based on the Centers for Disease Control's 1988 publication on recommendations for the prevention and containment of suicide clusters, as well as on limited personal experience. The CDC's pamphlet can be ordered from the Division of Injury Epidemiology and Control, Center for Environmental Health and Injury Control, Centers for Disease Control, Atlanta, Georgia 30333. Every community, school, mental health agency, and crisis center should be familiar with this publication.

The idea of contagion (the little understood process by which one suicide stimulates others to commit, attempt, or think about suicide) is not new. Recorded episodes of contagion-driven suicides date back several hundred years. More recently, researchers have learned a few things we all need to know:

• Contagion (however it works) leads to clusters of suicidal behavior, often resulting in unnecessary deaths by suicide.

• Clusters occur almost entirely among young people.

- Clusters account for about 3% of the suicides in young people, although figures in some individual states run as high as 13%.

- Two groups seem especially vulnerable: close friends of a suicide victim, and kids with depression or serious behavioral problems.

- Of all the suicides we might anticipate based on risk factors and assessments, cluster suicides might be the most preventable.

- Any person who dies as part of a cluster should never be assumed to have died simply because of the death of another. The reasons for suicide are always complex and the final act is always multi-determined.

Based on the work of Biblarz and Biblarz (personal communication), here is a brief description of a theory of contagion and what can be done to minimize its effects:

- Suicide contagion is a process in which a person's suicide or suicidal behavior affects others so that they also engage in such behavior; the behavior of the model may be witnessed directly, or it may be heard about in reports or stories, which may in turn be real or fictional.

- Suicide cluster is a group of suicides that take place in a short period of time, and that is significantly higher than expected (compared to base rates).

As noted, suicide contagion can take many forms and does not, automatically, lead to further suicides *per se*. It is enough to remember that one suicide in a population of youths can put the idea of suicide as a solution front and center in the minds of other young people, potentially enhancing the suicidal behavior of vulnerable youths already predisposed. Which young people are going to be negatively affected can be better guessed by considering the following:

• A good percentage of the young people who hear about a suicide are already suicidal.

• A good percentage of young people who hear about a suicide are clinically depressed, and, therefore, vulnerable to a suggestion of how to stop suffering.

• Some percentage of the young people who hear about a suicide will be positively identified with the youth who died.

The Biblarz team suggests that for contagion to take hold, certain necessary conditions must be met: a high affective environment, some identification with the model, individual vulnerability, and the perception that suicide is an adequate, or even optimal, solution to the problems of the model.

Assuming there has been a completed suicide, what can we do to minimize contagion?

STEP ONE: Don't panic. If you're the responsible adult in what appears to be a high-risk situation for more suicidal behavior following a completed suicide by a youth in your community (however your "community" is defined), now is the time be calm, cool, collected, and empathic. But mostly calm. Emotional neutrality—not another person veering out of control—is what young people need.

STEP TWO: Identify all the kids you're worried about: those with suicide attempt, talk, or gesture histories; those who've been acting out; the depressed ones; all the ones you (or anybody else) know are in some kind of emotional trouble at home or with friends or the law. If in a school setting, the school counselors, coaches or teachers, and administrators know just about every vulnerable child.

STEP THREE: Get all the smart people together and lay out a plan. A good plan for minimizing contagion includes the following components:

1) Individual, one-on-one counseling for the kids at risk. You may (will) need to outreach some of them.

2) Pick a single spokesperson to deal with the media (if present). The less said the better, especially about the method used.

3) Minimize publicity. For example, don't close the school or center, have any special assemblies, or otherwise call attention to the fact that someone died by suicide. A prepared statement about the suicide can be read to each class of students at the same time—thus controlling, in part, the rumor mill and its attendant hysteria.

4) The suicide itself should not be discussed in positive terms. No "I'm sure David is much happier now," or "At least all her problems are behind her now."

5) Do nothing to romanticize the suicide, sensationalize it, or otherwise allow it to be idealized in some Romeo and Juliet fashion. Suicide is, despite its occasional positive hype, still a lousy decision.

When asked about how to handle a youth suicide in the classroom setting, I've advised that, since the subject cannot be avoided without scaring kids even more, classroom teachers devote up to five minutes or so to the death. No more. Lead with a prepared statement and then cut off the chatter by acknowledging in calm tones that it is a true tragedy, that many of us feel sad, frightened, hurt, and even angry.

Last, I advise that teachers invite any children who wish to stay after class to talk to do so, or to take them personally to a school counselor or nurse. If school counselors are available, having them prepped and waiting for referrals after the announcement can head off hysteria. Outreaching distraught children (both those you see as well as the ones you "hear" about) is indicated. Likewise, if a troubled and troublesome child begins to act out after a suicide, this is probably not the time to send him or her home, threaten expulsion, and otherwise jeopardize what is, too often, the most important emotional support system a child has (the school).

As the affective environment will get no higher than at the funeral (the first for most young people), having plenty of calm, empathic adults around is strongly recommended— especially for junior high and young high school students.

Contract (No-Suicide)

Reviewed in depth elsewhere in the sections on intervention and treatment, a No-Suicide Contract is essentially an agreement between an interventionist or therapist and a suicidal person that, for some specified period of time, the suicidal person will not take his or her life.

Sometimes better termed a "no-harm" contract, the essential elements involve a commitment between two people that one of them will offer help while the other one agrees to keep living. Contracts seem to work partly because they reduce confusion, suggest at least someone is in control of events, involve mutual commitments between two human beings, and because, as is our nature, we tend to honor our agreements with others—even with people we've just met.

Countertransference

Earlier, in the sections on treatment, I have written about countertransference as it affects the therapy of suicidal people. Here, I will simply define it as those often intense feelings we develop toward others which, if we understood them better, we would know come from ourselves, not from other people.

For example, an older man unconsciously reminds us of our father and we treat him with respect or hostility, depending on how well we got along with our own father. An angry teenager reminds us of our own child, or ourselves when we were younger—a self we didn't like very much. Unaware of where our strong feelings are coming from, it is well to remember that people in a suicide crisis typically generate very strong feelings in us. Usually sympathy and understanding, but sometimes fear and resentment. The fear and resentment come from feeling manipulated, threatened, and otherwise put at emotional risk for being made responsible for someone else's life.

Basically, we need to know this is going to happen, is happening, and that *no matter what,* we need to stay in emotional neutral as much as possible. One way to keep from over-reacting is to acknowledge we are having strong feelings and that this is proof positive the suicidal person is in a great deal of pain—otherwise he or she wouldn't be stirring us up so much.

Having had my commitment and genuine concern for suicidal people tested many times, I can assure you some of them are very good at trying to confirm the world's loneliest hypothesis: People are no damned good. When a suicidal person is being especially nasty, difficult, contrary, and threatening, that's the perfect time to sit back, reflect on your feelings, and plan to share them later with a supervisor or a colleague.

Depression

Too many people conclude that depression automatically leads to thoughts of suicide and a heightened risk of suicide. The two terms—suicide and depression—are so closely linked that many thousands of people at risk of suicide who are not depressed go unnoticed. In fact, depression as the primary etiological factor in suicide represents only a little better than half the variance, i.e., you don't have to be depressed to be suicidal.

But it helps. Since about 15% of all depressed people will die by suicide, and about two-thirds of all suicides are associated with primary depressive illness, depression, in one form or another, is enemy number one.

Depression typically leads to a loss of interest and pleasure in usual activities and/or dysphoria (negative affective state), helplessness, feelings of worthlessness and low self-esteem and, eventually, an utter sense of hopelessness. As we all know, hopelessness kills.

The bad news about depression is that while it is as common as the common cold, recent polls by the National Mental Health Association indicate the following:

• Of the millions of Americans who suffer from depression, only 30% ever seek treatment.

- Among family members who recognize depression in their loved ones, 43% say they believe depression is a personal weakness, not a treatable illness.

- Better than one in ten of us will experience a major depression at some time in our life, and about 25% of all adults already have.

- The cost of depression to the economy is about $27 billion; $17 billion in absenteeism alone.

Now the good news.

- Depression is easily, sometimes even quickly, treated.

- Treatment is effective in better than 80% of the cases.

- Even untreated, most people finally get over a depressive episode—usually within nine to 13 months.

- Both talk and medical therapies work with depression.

- With depression successfully treated, hopelessness fades and people survive.

The Diagnosis

Without going into a lot of clinical detail here, depression can be characterized by a sad or melancholy mood, diminished interest in usual activities, and five or more of the following symptoms that last two weeks or longer: feeling tired despite adequate rest; changes in sleeping or eating patterns; sadness, breaking into tears for no apparent reason; loss of sex drive; lack of enthusiasm; inability to concentrate; feeling unwanted or guilty; and thinking life is not worth living.

The great majority of depressed people will experience the following six symptoms: reduced energy, trouble sleeping, diurnal mood swings (a.m. worse, improves in p.m.), impaired attention and concentration, inability to think well, and memory problems. A simple diagnosis to make, you can spot it in the sagged shoulders, the teary eye and, if you listen, you can hear it in the sigh.

Depression is a miserable, debilitating illness that no one should be blamed for. You don't get it because you are weak-minded, did something wrong, or because you're stupid. Blaming the victim only makes depression worse.

Since all depressed people are at some risk of suicide (let alone making poor party guests), this group of undetected, undiagnosed, and untreated people represents a huge public health problem for all of us. Therefore, anything we can do to de-stigmatize depression with an individual patient, his or her family, or the general public, will be great service to human kind.

Divorce

Anytime a divorce is threatened or in progress, family members are at increased risk. Let's begin with the children.

The Kids

A number of researchers have pointed out that children of divorce are at significantly higher risk of suicide than children from non-divorced parents. The sad formula seems to be: Where the home is broken, so is the heart of the child.

Children often blame themselves for their parents' divorce and are, therefore, at acute risk for suicidal ideation and action during the early phases of separation and divorce. Many child experts (of which I am not one) feel that divorce is more difficult to accept than death. As death is final, a child can grieve and get on; but with divorce the pain seems as though it will never end—especially if you have blamed yourself for your parents' wretchedness, suffering, fighting, and hatred.

There are several questions to ask of a child whose parents are divorcing. Among these are:

1) Has any parent or grandparent modeled suicidal behavior? (The National Institute of Mental Health recently found one out of every four people who attempt suicide has a family member who has attempted suicide.)

2) Has either of the parents (whether stepparent or natural) consciously or unconsciously blamed the child for the divorce?

3) Would the child's suicide somehow "solve" the parents' problems? (This does not have be a real solution; only a perceived one.)

4) Is either of the parents mentally ill? Depressed or angry or psychotic parents who threaten suicide greatly increase the risk of suicidal behavior in their children.

5) Does the child believe anyone wants him or her dead, i.e., would dying satisfy one or both parents in some perverse way?

No expert on children or adolescents, I have worked with a few and have consulted on many more cases. My bottom line is this: No child should have to die because his or her parents can't find a way to get along. Since the parents are often in the worst possible position to help a suicidal child (they may even use the child's suicidality as evidence that the departing spouse should return), it is up to us to not only help the child survive, but put the disintegrating family into some kind of healing environment.

The Adults

As written about elsewhere in the treatment section, a careful study of the relationship between a couple threatening a separation and divorce can, very simply, prevent one or the other of them dying by suicide. In a few cases, a homicide/suicide may even be prevented.

Basically, of the two sexes, men do not handle divorce nearly as well as women. Therefore, if it is a woman leaving a man (and he has a history of intense jealousy, unrecognized dependency needs, and doesn't want her to go), you have a potentially lethal situation for both of them. The more final her actions (moving out, seeing a lawyer, dating another man, etc.), the higher the risk. The worst kind of injury to the male ego and the one which may precipitate a suicide crisis, being left by a woman is something, as Winston Churchill might have said, "Up with which I will not put!"

While women being left are often plagued by suicidal feelings, at least they are more likely to seek help, make non-lethal gestures or attempts, and otherwise cry out when they are knee deep in the swamp. Men, on the other hand, won't even whimper until they're up to their necks in alligators... if then. Which leads me to suggest the following strategies for accessing men at risk of suicide who are going through an unwanted separation and/or divorce:

1)   Cultural considerations notwithstanding, be forthright. If you're working with the departing wife, don't count on her to get him in (she may be too angry at him to want to save him). Rather, with her permission, call

the husband yourself and invite him in for a consultation, either with you or a colleague.

2) If the wife won't give permission for you to talk to her soon-to-be ex—and you believe he is at substantial risk of suicide based on her descriptions of fact—consider calling or going to see him anyway. Better to have an angry wife than a dead husband.

3) When you get face to face with a man who is being left, don't pull your punches. Most men appreciate a no-nonsense approach. Blunt questions will get you further than delicate ones.

Shattered men are a kind of specialty with me and, more than once, I've made home visits to see men who I knew to be in an acute suicidal crisis. They were armed, but not dangerous—that is, to anyone but themselves. To carry off such interventions it has always helped me to think of desperate, despairing men as frightened little boys who have just suffered a major blow to their self-esteem. They'll mend just like anyone else, but you have to give them the chance. Of course, you may have to work around and through and over a great deal of male pride to save a life, but it can be done.

Men and Humor

A little humor seems to help with men. I once asked a highly suicidal man, "How are you going to do it?" He replied, "With malathion." So I said, "What are you, a bug?" And he said, "No, I'm a life member of the National Rifle Association and we're getting enough bad press about the misuse of firearms as it is." Our laughter cut the tension instantly.

As it turned out, this man was a gun collector and had ample means of self-destruction. As it also turned out his relationship problems were quite repairable and his depression quite treatable. He survived.

As noted, we are much more likely to hear from women in distress and, therefore, we have a better chance at preventing a suicide. But as women can be resistant to seeking help as well, there is nothing sexist about my recommendations here.

Last, anecdotal reports suggest that if a mother becomes suicidal, she is less likely to kill her spouse and then herself, and more likely to kill her children and then herself. Although responsibility for children is generally a buffer against suicide in women, every care should be taken to see that any children in these highly volatile situations are safe.

Drug Abuse

Most of the research on the relationship of substance abuse to suicide has focused on the role alcohol plays as a risk factor. However, several studies now point to the increased risk drug users incur when they attempt to solve life's problems through chemistry. The causal relationship between drug abuse and suicide is complicated, but necessary action to reduce the risk to those using is simple: Get them clean and sober.

Here are a few facts to have at hand when you are dealing with someone who uses drugs:

• In the most comprehensive study ever conducted on the relationship of drugs to suicide (the San Diego Suicide Study), 58% of 283 completed suicides during the years 1981 to 1983 had a history drug abuse. True, some of them had had psychiatric problems as well, but 39%

carried the principle diagnosis of substance abuse alone. Subsequent studies have verified these findings.

• In many jurisdictions, overdoses of illicit drugs are not certified as suicides unless there is clear and convincing evidence the person had an intention to die. Thus, suicide among drug abusers is probably grossly under-reported—especially among minorities.

• Several studies suggest the risk to death by suicide among drug abusers may be 10 to 20 times higher than that for the general population.

• Although the research is less than perfect, suicide among drug abusers appears more closely associated with poly-substance abuse, the presence of a second psychiatric problem (often depression), poor social adjustment, and any life threatening illness.

• Being under the influence of drugs or alcohol increases the likelihood of an impulsive act.

All these data and findings are only helpful as background information to help you be a better informed interventionist or therapist. When you have a real live person in front of you, and in spite of having just helped him or her make the association between substance abuse and the risk of suicide, you must now deal with a different reality: This person probably doesn't want to quit drugs. If he or she could have "just said no," believe me, he or she would have already done it and wouldn't be talking to you.

My personal approach with addicts and alcoholics is to level with them right from the start; even say, for example, "If you keep using, you're at a 10 to 20 times greater risk of death by suicide than people who don't use."

I'm not saying this to frighten them (although I would frighten the bejeesus out of them if it would help them get clean), but I figure they ought to know the facts. Addicts generally don't like facts, but that's their problem, not mine. As I see it, my job is to share with them what I know. If information about smoking, unprotected sex in the age of AIDS, and how to keep your cholesterol count low can save lives and lengthen the days we've got, why shouldn't drug abusers hear the facts? Besides, you never know what it is you will say or do that, in fact, will help someone choose to turn it around and go on living.

A Word of Warning

Unless you are a drug treatment specialist or a recovering professional person who works in this field and are, therefore, accustomed to the kinds of deceptions and magnificent maneuvers addicts have at their disposal to put you off the track to their own recovery, beware! Addicts and alcoholics count heavily on ignorance and innocence among helping professionals to assist them in their denial that anything "really serious" is going on with their use of substances.

"I only take a little toke of grass to relax." "I never inject, so how bad can a little coke be?" "Me? Drink? Why I only drink after five p.m., and then only wine." The little toke turns out to be a 24-hour stoner trip, the coke up the nose is a \$200-a-day habit, and the wine after dinner is a half-gallon of cheap, fortified Mad Dog 20-20. Advice: don't be dumb. And don't, unconsciously and unwittingly, aid and abet the very illness that may eventually kill the patient anyway: addiction.

Unless you know something about addictions and how addicts think, feel, and operate, now is the perfect time to get a consult, make a referral, or otherwise get this person to someone who knows the score. Because if you don't take the addict's addiction seriously, I can guarantee you he or she won't either. And that can spell disaster.

Elderly

As most human service workers know (or should know), the elderly are more at risk for suicide than any other age group. According to the National Center for Health Statistics, 25% of all suicides are committed by persons over 65. And according to a recent report by the Centers for Disease Control, it is getting worse. There was, at last report, a 21% increase in elderly suicide between the years 1980 and 1986.

A few facts to stick in your hat:

- The suicide rate for persons over age 55 is 50% higher than for the general population. And it is going up.

- Older people are more successful than other age groups when they attempt to kill themselves.

- One in four attempts in this age group is successful, compared to a 1 in 200 ratio for the general population.

- The majority of elderly people who take their lives *are not* terminally ill.

- As a rule, elderly people send signals that they wish to die just like everyone else. The trouble is, too few people take them seriously, including (and sometimes especially) their doctors.

Further, according to David C. Clark, a psychologist at Rush Presbyterian/St. Luke's Medical Center, 90% of the elderly who commit suicide are suffering from mental illness. Over 60% of these are depressed, while another large group are alcoholic—both conditions strongly associated with eventual suicide, and both conditions which are highly treatable.

Rather than try to figure out what might be going on here from a national perspective, let's just cut to the pertinent, life-saving things you need to know to do a better job with older people.

Reducing Suicide Risk in the Elderly

The first thing to remember about suicide and the elderly is that, for them as well as anyone else, suicide solves an "insoluble " problem or problems. The problem(s) may or may not be insoluble; it only matters that the person believes it is insoluble.

The second thing to remember is that elderly people generally do not ask for help—with soluble or insoluble problems. The secret code among the old seems to be: If you can't fix it yourself, it can't be fixed.

Challenge: As helping professionals, how are we going to get to those who need us to help them fix a problem?

The answer is, I'm afraid, that those elderly most in need of solutions to quite soluble problems are not getting help—otherwise we might not be experiencing the present suicide epidemic in this age group.

In a recent unpublished study of suicide rates in my own area (where our mental health center has a decade-old model program for outreaching, finding, and treating the frail, multiply-impaired, at-risk elderly), we recently learned our county now has the lowest elderly suicide rate in the state of Washington (16/100,000). Maybe we shouldn't take all the credit, but because our aggressive outreach to those elderly most in need has become a national model for long-term care, we will take some. (For more information on this program, contact: Spokane Community Mental Health Center at (509) 838-4651. Information packets are available.)

The key thing to keep in mind is that suicidal elderly are very unlikely to self-refer. And why should they? You may put them in a nursing home. Or think them "crazy." Circumventing and overcoming these fears through relationship building on common ground is absolutely essential to good service delivery. Therefore, if you want to prevent the elderly from killing themselves, you're going to have to go to them.

Consider some of the unique problems the elderly must often face: retirement and loss of self-esteem associated with work; physiological changes; poor health; economic hardships; powerlessness; loss of a spouse; repeated bereavements; dementia (in themselves or a loved one); helplessness (can't fix the roof anymore); social isolation; fear of being institutionalized; and from too many of us, ageism and the associated pain of discrimination. Even worse, there is a growing public sentiment by some in our society that the elderly owe it to the rest of us to kill themselves.

But there is plenty of room for hope. Since the elderly suffer from the same mental and emotional problems as the rest of us, and since we know that medications and counseling and psychotherapy can save lives, we only need to get these same services to the elderly. Also, since older people in trouble are not ignorant about their coming to the end of their lives, they are not hesitant to discuss death and/or their suicidal thoughts. If providers and health care professionals would just ask, they would get an answer I once got from a 74-year-old lady who was in lots of trouble with emphysema, depression, and alcoholism: "Of course I've been thinking about suicide. Do I look stupid to you?"

Here, from my notes on a lecture I give on counseling older people, are a few helpful strategies and tips:

1) A comprehensive medical workup should precede everything else we undertake. Since depression is rampant among this age group (often disguised as dementia), a comprehensive social, psychological/psychiatric workup by skilled geriatric specialists is recommended. Where indicated, pharmacotherapy with depressed people is very effective.

2) Once you've found an elderly person in trouble (has problems he or she or they can't fix), round up supportive services: a visiting nurse, a repairman for the front porch, hot meals, and medical care. Get legal problems settled, find a lost family member, get a neighbor to help where possible. In general, the counselor or case manager's job is to take care of the fundamentals of survival, including safety, security, and medical care. Like everyone else, the elderly need hope to survive; supply just a little and they will choose to go on.

3) Many elderly who believe they've just been given a terminal diagnosis are at acute risk of suicide. The word "cancer" can strike a morbid fear into the hearts of some—thus propelling them into a suicidal crisis. This need not happen.

   As the mere belief that one has a terminal illness can lead to a suicide, it is our job to immediately clarify this diagnosis and its accuracy from the primary care provider. Too often the medical profession (maybe because of its own fear and denial about telling people they are gravely ill) doesn't always communicate clearly in these highly emotional encounters. Or maybe the listener hears something that wasn't said. Either way, the result can be that some elderly people will kill themselves on the basis of a misunderstanding, e.g., they didn't have cancer after all. By actively exploring these fears and verifying diagnoses and prognostications, at least a few precipitous suicides might be averted.

4) When it comes to suicide, the elderly don't fool around. Any attempt at suicide by an elderly person should put us on full alert. Generally, a failed suicide attempt will reflect a lack of planning, not insufficient intent or determination. The elderly tend to use more lethal methods than younger people and, being much more experienced problem solvers, they often know what it takes to kill a person.

In general, and compared with other age groups, there is often little ambivalence to work with in the suicidal elderly person. With their life expectancy already foreshortened, you have to work fast, hard, and as always, be bold.

Ethnic Issues

If the assessment, intervention, and treatment of suicidal people is difficult enough in the majority white population (where most of the clinical research has been done), the challenge of working with diverse minority populations is a real test of the interventionist's/therapist's skills. Not only must the helper know and understand broad cultural issues, but he or she must also understand subtle differences *within* ethnic groups.

For example, there are 40 different ethnic Asian-American groups; many, many Indian tribes; and several distinct Hispanic and African-American populations—each with unique cultural features, religious orientations, and specific views on the subject of suicide. As experienced clinicians know, depression and hopelessness are expressed in quite different ways in different cultures and, so too, is the suicidal wish. Scientific data on even the most fundamental risk factors among various ethnic groups is scarce and, in many cases, non-existent. Even reports of suicidal death to national data banks often lump reports into White, African-American, or Other—thus neglecting dozens of minority groups.

As an example of how bad data can stereotype entire ethnic groups, consider that much of the research on Indian suicide has been on clusters (where two or more native people died over a short period of time in a single social environment). As a result, there is a generally held popular perception that Indian suicide is epidemic among all native peoples. This is simply not true.

From a recent meeting at the National Institute of Mental Health, a summary finding indicated that, for example, among the Shoshone, only five families contributed to all suicides reported in that tribe. The Hopi have a very low rate of suicide, and the only reported suicides were among Hopi who had married out of the tribe. To say that all Indian peoples everywhere are at a high risk of suicide is to practice the most blatant kind of racial stereotyping.

While space does not permit addressing all the relevant training issues to help a therapist become culturally competent to identify, assess, and treat minority people at risk of suicide, I strongly suggest that unless you know a good deal about the culture of the minority person you are assessing or treating for suicidality, you get a consult from someone who does.

For example, it can prove very helpful to know that when a Northern Plains Indian says, "I'm going to follow the spirit trail," he does not mean he is going to take an L.S.D. trip. Likewise, when a practicing Buddhist (depending on the sect) says that his family will feel only "sympathy and regret" if he goes now, "to see our ancestors," he may well be speaking the cultural truth.

From several recent, but hardly comprehensive studies on ethnicity and suicide (see reference section for sources and additional readings on suicide and mental health), here are a few findings that may prove useful:

Asians

From an article by Yoshitomo Takahashi, here are some helpful recommendations on working with suicidal Asian patients. As the gulf between the Occidental and Oriental worlds is wide, non-Asians need to be especially cognizant of the following differences:

Language. Depending on the Asian patient's familiarity with English, major problems can accrue when a non-Asian therapist simply assumes that because the patient is "in America," he or she now understands English. Except for native Asian-Americans, or that minority of immigrants who have studied English intensively, there is considerable risk that the therapist may become frustrated or bored with the patient's inability to clearly communicate his or her problems or feelings—thus making rapport and a working alliance impossible.

Different Logic. Whereas Americans pride themselves on being open, direct, and to-the-point, Asian logic is more circular, indirect, and subtle. Candor can be, therefore, a liability. Likewise, going directly to the heart of a problem may not work, especially if there is a shadow of shame attached to that problem. Occidental therapists need to slow down, wait for things to emerge, and take their foot off the interview accelerator.

Reticence. While American patients are often willing to expose their pain and failings readily, this is not so with Asian patients. Disciplined to evaluate the reactions of others very carefully before exposing themselves, silent Asian patients are not being difficult. Rather, they are waiting for the correct moment and context in which to speak.

Atypical Depressive Symptoms. According to several researchers, Chinese people tend to show more atypical physical symptoms when depressed. Some writers point to the lack of a "language of emotion" to account for this culturally appropriate way of communicating distress and depression. This expression of depression appears to hold for other Asian groups as well.

Mental Illness. Asians in general attach a great deal of shame to mental illness. Thus, even the most depressed people may be unwilling to seek professional services. The whole notion of psychiatry and the "talking cure" is quite alien to most recently arrived immigrants. Self-help, for example, is a uniquely Christian and American value. Compared with the Asian culture, where family ties are close and people in trouble are extended support and help without asking, the idea of either reaching out for assistance or even helping yourself solve some problem or other, is quite foreign.

Interdependence, Submissiveness, and Families. If autonomy is a highly prized American value, just the opposite is true of most Asians. Getting along with family and friends, not sticking out in a crowd, knowing you are helpful to others and can be helped by those around you... these are personal characteristics prized by Asians. Harmony with others is much more important than ego—which makes traditional psychotherapy (whose goals are individuation, freedom from family, self-directedness, etc. etc.) seem both bizarre and frightening to many Asians.

Where the family bond is still strong, involvement of family members becomes crucial to suicide intervention and therapy with Asian patients. Not only does the patient expect their involvement, family members expect to be involved. Confidentiality (a highly regarded Constitutional guarantee understood by all Americans) is not even a developed concept among Asian immigrants. In fact, in many Asian countries, no such word exists to describe one's own privacy, let alone a right to it.

African-Americans

- Suicide among African-Americans is largely a phenomenon of youth. Suicide peaks among African-Americans during the young adult years (25-34) and tapers off thereafter. Compared with old white guys (where suicide increases each year), old African-American guys have apparently figured out how to relax and enjoy autumn, fall, and winter.

- Suicide among African-American youths has more than doubled in the past 25 years, and is now the third leading cause of death.

- The actual suicide rate among African-Americans may be grossly under-reported. For example, some researchers feel that African-Americans, compared with other groups, may set up "deadly confrontations" with the police in order to provoke lethal retaliation, thus leading to victim-precipitated suicides. Where political agendas are evident, some of these "suicides" would meet the definition of "revolutionary" or "fatalistic" suicides (á la Durkheim's terms), but would be counted as homicides.

• Given the cultural differences in the expression of depression, hopelessness, and suicidal intent, African-American youths who are verbally abusive, sullen, hostile, and angry should *not* be assumed to be safe. Rather, just the opposite may be true.

• Expressions of hopelessness and despair among African-American youths may take the form of excessive risk taking, sexual promiscuity, substance abuse, and delinquency—including confrontations with the police.

• The greatest problem faced by suicidal African-Americans (youth and older) is access to services. Simply put, the very services that could help them save their lives by helping them solve the problems for which suicide seems such a tempting solution are too often unavailable, under-funded, or culturally inappropriate.

Hispanics and Mexican-Americans

• Again, too little research has been done with these diverse cultures to add much to our knowledge base. However, from what is known, the base rate for suicide among Hispanics and Mexican-Americans is considerably lower than for non-Hispanic whites.

   Note: Since much of this research is based on Spanish surnames alone, other non-Hispanic races may be counted in the figures; therefore, the true base rate for this group may be even lower.

- The patterns of suicidal behavior (ideation, threats, gestures, and completions) parallel those of non-Hispanic whites. For example, women attempt more than men, men complete more than women, and the presence of psychiatric illness (especially depression) increases risk. Being single, divorced, and educated are also risk factors.

- It appears Mexico-born Mexican-Americans have an even lower rate of suicidal ideation than those Mexican-Americans born in the U.S.—suggesting strong cultural and religious ties serve as buffers to self-destruction.

- Biculturally sensitive prevention and treatment staff are highly indicated for this group, as are any measures to reduce barriers to the kinds of human services which would prevent suicidal thinking and feelings in the first place.

American Indians

- Where studied, suicide rates among different tribes and pueblos vary considerably. However, and as found in other racial groups, the rate among young people appears to be climbing.

  Note: Because of the rapid increase in the total population base of Native Americans (up from 220,000 in 1900 to 2,500,000 in 1980), there are large numbers of adolescents and young adults—the very age groups at great risk of death by accident, suicide, and homicide.

- Several studies show strong correlations between the rate of alcoholism, drug abuse, and suicide. As in other cultures, it is males who kill themselves in greater numbers.

- With adult unemployment as high as 90% in some tribes, many adolescents see no future. Thus, hopelessness runs high.

- The list of chronic stressors faced by many at-risk Native American youth include parental neglect and abuse, loss of cultural and family support through adoption (to non-Indian families), chronic poverty, lack of opportunity, and all the usual and customary crises associated with being an adolescent.

- Where pressures to join and blend in with the majority culture are great, and where there is extensive tribal conflict about keeping traditions or going away from them, more mental and emotional problems arise in those who must struggle with these choices. The rule seems to be that the greater the conflict between traditional Indian values and new Anglo values, the more difficult it is for youth to find a way to survive.

    However, in tribes where traditions are still intact, where the elders are still available and respected, and where the rites of passage and religious rituals are still honored, young people can find someone with whom they can identify and talk about their problems. Respected elders of both sexes may be the best suicide interventionists and therapists for these youths.

Finally, suicide always occurs in a cultural context, and that context is critical to understanding suicide's meaning, its purpose, its consequences for survivors, and even what ultimate purpose a suicide may serve. Cultures have preferred places to suicide, preferred methods, and people permitted to suicide under certain "preferred" circumstances: e.g., old Eskimo women, Cheyenne warriors, shamed Samurai, disgraced Generals, and writers whose talents for poetry and prose have shriveled and died (Hemingway, Plath, Mishima, Kawatata, Sexton, Woolf, and others). To ignore these contextual issues is to ignore what can prove, in the clinches, to be life-saving information for the interventionist and therapist.

Family History

Given the power of social learning among people and among generations, it is no surprise that suicide runs in families. More, since there is growing evidence of gene-linked vulnerability to depression, mood disorders, and possibly alcoholism (all of which figure prominently in the risk factors for suicide), getting a good family history for suicidality, depression, and alcoholism is essential to understanding the suicidal person.

Anytime you find a parent, sibling, uncle, grandparent, or other significant family member who completed a suicide, it is important to explore this in detail, help the suicidal person understand how he or she feels (or felt) about the suicide and whether, for example, his or her own suicide ideation resulted from the relative's suicide. Helping such victims distance themselves from such a model can be lifesaving. Joining a survivors' group can help accomplish this by coaxing out the frozen grief and bringing about the necessary healing through sharing.

Family Involvement

Other things being equal, families should be immediately involved in any suicidal crisis experienced by a member of that family. Contraindictions include the following:

- Where there is any motive or desire on the part of the suicidal person to hurt one or more family members through suicide, thereby leaving the guilt on the head of the survivor. Broaching the subject needs to take place, but maybe later rather than sooner. Once a therapeutic alliance has been built, such motives of vengeance and punishment can be explored with a more beneficial outcome.

- Where the revelation that one member of a family is suicidal may jeopardize the delicate relationship the interventionist or therapist has with the suicidal person. In a word, if the suicidal person threatens to suicide if you break confidence with a family member (but will go on living if you don't), then don't. Pacing, as always, is everything.

- When an announcement of the suicidality of one of the members of the family may trigger suicidality (or even homicidal risk) in other family members.

- When you, the interventionist/therapist, feel that such a revelation of intent to suicide will make the patient's living situation more lethal, not less.

To the degree suicidal threats, gestures, attempts, and communications are a measure of a "failure to communicate," a careful assessment of these failed familial communications should yield a rich trove of clinical information about how the family can best be assisted to survive. The decision to involve the family rests on clinical judgment, much assisted by a consult with a colleague or supervisor.

Fear Of Punishment (Risk Factor)

This entry is just a note to those working primarily with adolescents. Fear of punishment seems to be a major risk factor for youth. Being arrested for even a minor crime can, in the minds of some youth, be blown way out of proportion and, unfortunately, lead to an impulsive suicide. Every year jails and juvenile detention facilities experience suicides among young people who would rather die than face parental wrath. The wrath of the court is usually mild and seldom figures in the equation.

As a risk factor for adults, fear of punishment typically involves honorable men caught in the act of doing something dishonorable, e.g., stealing the company's money. It is interesting to note that in some times and places committing suicide because you lost a war, or made a stupid decision that hurt people who were counting on you, or otherwise implicated yourself in a harmful action against your community gave you the right to kill yourself. A few honorable Russian politicians, during the failed coup of 1991, took this course of action. Given a culture's tacit approval of these acts of honor, such suicides can rarely be prevented.

Gay (Homosexual)

The research literature on gays is quite clear: This is not a particularly kind culture in which to be homosexual. Officially, everyone knows homosexuality is no longer a form of psychopathology, but judging from the psychosocial stressors bearing down on those with alternative sexual lifestyles, you wouldn't know it.

Perhaps it is enough to say that if you are gay, you are automatically at higher risk of developing those signs,

symptoms, addictions, and emotional problems that come—
rather directly—from being alienated, disenfranchised,
misunderstood, and victimized by hostile attitudes and
actions directed toward you for something that is nobody's
business but your own. If you lost the love and support of
your family along the way, so much the worse for your
psychological and emotional well being.

If you are working with a gay person, here are a number
of things to think about:

• What is your attitude toward homosexuality? If you
   don't understand and can't relate to gay people
   (especially those youth who are only finding out they
   might be gay), you may have a great deal of trouble
   helping them deal with those stresses that have brought
   on thoughts of suicide.

• If the whole subject of homosexuality disgusts you, or
   so preoccupies your consciousness you can't *hear* what
   the person is saying, for Pete's sake refer the person to
   someone who can. There is one thing we know for
   certain the suicidal person doesn't need: another
   rejection.

• Consider where the person is in his or her life cycle and
   psychological development. Is he just learning he might
   be gay? Has she told her friends and family yet? Or has
   the person long ago accepted his or her sexual orientation
   and is perfectly at ease?

• It is very important to never project "homosexual
   problems" onto gays with real-life problems that have
   absolutely nothing to do with being gay. Just being
   homosexual does not a problem make; rather, it is
   attitudes toward this sexual orientation that are generally
   the problem.

- Like straight people, gays at risk of suicide may come from the same kinds of dysfunctional, alcoholic, abusive, brutish, and/or enmeshed pathological families as the rest of us. Such family-of-origin issues can be fertile ground for intervention and therapy—especially if the gay person has been rejected by those who were supposed to love him or her.

Teens at Special Risk

Now, for a moment, imagine you are a teenager in a family that is already dysfunctional, has gross homophobic hatreds, calls all homosexuals "queers," and no member of which would spend five seconds in the company of a gay person if he or she could help it. Now put yourself in the role of that boy as he finds out that, despite his wishing he could will away his feelings, he is probably gay. With no one to turn to, isolated, frightened, anticipating (accurately) rejection by the most significant people in his life, is it any wonder thoughts of self-destruction pop into his mind?

Such an impossible psychological spot may account for why suicide is reported to be the *leading* cause of death among young, male homosexuals. Hopeless about changing the attitudes of others, nature, and hopeless about finding help and understanding in a straight world, what's a fellow to do?

The trick, as I see it, is not to let anyone kill him- or herself over a problem of sexual identity or some passing crisis about one's sexual nature. These things, as they say, will pass. If an agonized Michelangelo had killed himself over a crisis of sexual identity, how much poorer would we all be? Or an Oscar Wilde? Or a Martina Navratilova? Or any of the thousands of gays who have given, give, and will give so much to the world?

Holidays

Despite the popular assumption that major holidays are a risk factor for suicide, just the opposite appears to be true. According to a research team at the Department of Sociology at the University of California at San Diego, Phillips and Wills examined the fluctuation of 188,047 suicides from 1973 to 1979 before, during, and after major holidays. Here are the findings:

- There was an annual average of 102 fewer suicides in the period surrounding the holidays. An unusually low rate was found for Memorial Day, Thanksgiving, and Christmas.

- Another set of holidays (New Year's Day, July 4th, and Labor Day) were associated with low risk before the holiday, but a high risk just afterward.

- All risk groups were equally affected, except for white teenagers.

Implications:

- It would seem being surrounded by family lowers suicide risk. Most interventionists know this, at least intuitively.

- Teenagers may be the exception to this rule; therefore, a little special attention to at-risk young people during the holidays would seem in order.

- People helpers need to shift their focus from the pre-holiday Christmas blues (when the media makes the most noise about those without) to the post-holiday let-down period when isolated, depressed, and suicidal people apparently feel the most pain.

Personal
Note: Having volunteered to work the Christmas to New Year's shift at my mental health center for better than 20 years, I can tell you that from Christmas Eve to New Year's Day things are very quiet.

Hopelessness

Many authors have written about hopelessness and its role in suicidal behavior. Of these, Aaron Beck has probably done the most experimental work. His productive output in the area of learned helplessness, depression, and hopelessness can be found in his many fine books.

For our purposes here, it is enough to note that hopelessness is the utter feeling that no matter what you might try to do, nothing will work; that no matter what you would like or need in this life, you will not get it; that despite being relatively intelligent, all your decisions are stupid ones; that even though people say they love and appreciate you, you believe in your heart of hearts that people don't really mean what they say. And on and on and on it goes. People suffering acute and chronic hopelessness have been gradually ground down to a sense of utter futility and despair. They are, therefore, not much fun at parties.

While I have written extensively about how to treat hopelessness in the section on therapy, here are few important things to remember:

- In simplistic terms, hopelessness is a temporary condition born out of cognitive distortions and mistakes (mental misunderstandings and errors in thinking and logic).

- Not everyone who is suicidal is seriously hopeless; some suicidal behavior is an effort to gain better control of one's social environment and/or significant others.

- Hopelessness is more strongly related to suicide than depression. Hopeless people do not so much want to change the world as get out of it entirely. Therefore, where hopelessness is high, intention to die is also high.

- Hopelessness includes such things as pessimism, self-hate, and a chronic sense of failure as a human being. Melancholy and sadness may be present as well.

- Often, a state of hopelessness is what people have logically talked themselves into; therefore, a mood-altering drug may not work as quickly or well as someone (like you) who can talk the person back out again.

    Note: Having worked with a number of hopeless, highly logical but suicidal lawyers, this can be more fun than you ever imagined.

One thing to keep in mind is that lots of studies on hopeless people point to the fact that such folks do not solve problems well. They experience more faulty logic, reach more wrong conclusions, are more rigid, and can't—sometimes for the very life of them—figure out how to extricate themselves from some puzzle or other. Plagued by distorted beliefs, bad information, overgeneralization, and inflexibility, they are in the worst possible shape to make a life and death decision. Therefore, as interventionists and therapists, we need to use the *illogic* of their own condition, situation, and thinking to help them save their lives.

Aaron Beck has created a very useful scale to measure hopelessness. It is brief, reliable, face-valid, and very helpful in both clinical and research settings. Entitled, *The Hopelessness Scale*, copies and scoring instructions can be obtained from: Center for Cognitive Therapy, 133 South 36th Street, Philadelphia, PA 19104.

Media—How To Handle It

The primary concern with suicide and the media is the possible effect one has upon the other. Suicides are news, and news of suicides may trigger suicidal behavior in vulnerable people. The goal of those researching and working in this area is to first understand the connection (if any) between the media's portrayal of suicide in either hard news or fiction, and the occurrence of additional suicides (the contagion effect).

Clearly, if news of a youth suicide is dramatized, sensationalized, and framed as an attractive alternative to the wretched life of the adolescent, such a portrayal might reasonably lead other suicide-receptive youth to take some sort of action—especially if the method is described in enough detail to permit imitative learning of the "how-to" part of the final act.

Because the media (print, radio, and TV) feel strongly about the rights of the people to know the news, it is sometimes tough to convince them not to make matters worse by over-playing a suicide in their medium. However, my personal experience with the media (all kinds) is that they are usually quite sensitive to this issue and will, with just a little education, cooperate fully.

The following guidelines are taken directly from the American Association of Suicidology's recommendations for those who deal with the media regarding a suicide in their community, and for those who speak on the subject to the public:

> 1) To discourage imitative or copycat suicides, it is important to avoid or minimize:

- Reporting specific details of the method.

- Descriptions of a suicide as unexplainable,

  e.g., "He had everything going for him."

- Reporting romanticized versions of the reasons for the suicide (s), e.g., "We want to be together for all eternity."

- Simplistic reasons for the suicide, e.g., "Boy commits suicide because he has to wear braces."

In addition, the print media can reduce the imitative effect by:

- Printing story on inside page.

- If story must appear on first page, print it below the fold.

- Avoid the word "suicide" in the headline.

- Avoid printing a photo of the person who committed suicide.

It is important to report a suicide in a straightforward manner so that the suicide does not appear exciting. Reports should not make the suicidal person appear admirable, nor should they seem to approve of the suicide.

2) To encourage prevention of suicide, it
is helpful to:

- Present alternatives to suicide,
e.g., calling a suicide prevention
center, getting counseling, etc.

- Whenever possible, present
examples of positive outcomes of
people in suicidal crises.

- Provide information on community resources for those who
may be suicidal or who know
people who are.

- Include a list of clues to suicidal
behavior...

The Association's recommendations go on to suggest
speakers and presenters list the known clues to suicide and
that they recommend open, frank discussions among those
concerned. Maybe most helpful, public speakers should be
prepared to give out community-specific information about
where to get help.

Public Presentation of Suicide

If you give an open-to-the public presentation on the
subject of suicide you will almost always draw someone
suicidal to the audience. When ending a presentation, and at
the end of your talk, make it a point to invite anyone in the
audience who would like to stay and chat more in depth to
do so. I've met many suicidal people this way and, into the
bargain, have then been able to refer them on for help. If
you're expecting a big public crowd, it is a good idea to take
along some extra professional staff to meet with whoever

surfaces—especially if there has been a recent, high-profile suicide in your community.

For a more in-depth report on how community officials can work with the media to minimize the likelihood of imitative suicides among adolescents and young adults, a copy of *Recommendations from a Workshop on Suicide Contagion and Reporting Suicide* may be obtained by writing to the Public Health Foundation, 1220 L Street, NW, Washington, D.C. 20005.

Myths

Maybe because suicide sometimes seems such an unknowable human endeavor, many myths and misconceptions have accompanied the subject down through the centuries. Francine Klagsburn, in her book, *Too Young to Die*, notes the following most commonly accepted "truths" about suicide:

- The person who talks a great deal about suicide won't actually attempt it.

- A person who tries and fails to commit suicide probably will not attempt suicide again.

- If a person has been very depressed for a time, says there's nothing to live for, and wants to die, then abruptly begins to act relaxed and cheerful, one can safely assume that his or her suicidal thoughts have passed.

- The individual who attempts suicide has got to be crazy.

- Once someone decides to kill himself, nothing can stop him.

- Statistics indicate that suicide strikes mostly among the very wealthy because they are so jaded and bored with life.

- Suicide runs in one's family.

- Mention suicide to suicidal persons and it gives them ideas.

- It cannot be suicide if the person didn't leave a note.

- They loved each other so much, they wanted to die together.

As you've no doubt guessed, none of these statements is true. Unfortunately, too many people who know someone in a suicide crisis believe they *are* true. As a result, such beliefs can do a great deal of damage. In my own therapeutic work with families, I have often heard people say of a son or daughter who took his or her life by suicide, "They tried it once, so there was nothing any of us could do." Another woman said of a nephew who fatally shot himself, "His mother committed suicide, so he had to." These are, frankly, beliefs that can kill.

Parasuicidal

Introduced by Norman Kreitman, "parasuicidal" is a term used to describe suicidal behavior that, on close inspection, appears to have little likelihood of resulting in death. Kreitman defined parasuicide as a non-fatal act in which an individual deliberately causes self-injury or ingests a substance in excess of any prescribed or generally recognized therapeutic dosage. As a clearer term to describe attempted suicide with a low level of lethality, only about 10% to 20% of parasuicidal people go on to complete a suicide.

Parasuicidal people, generally, want less to die than to gain control of events and other people. They are typically going through some major upheaval but have not experienced the kind of grinding down, corrosive effect of multiple, unrelenting losses and setbacks. Such behavior occurs more frequently in females, decreases with age, and tends to be more impulsive. Such people are also more hopeful than hopeless. And, into the bargain, they tend to be more angry and less depressed than the seriously suicidal.

None of this means that such parasuicidal threats and gestures should be taken lightly, but it does suggest that less dramatic therapeutic responses may be appropriate. For example, psychiatric hospitalization may be contraindicated. Medications will probably not be necessary. Heroic efforts by caregivers may result in a worsening of the situation, not an improvement. Talk therapies, relationship-focused counseling, and gentle but firm confrontation and limit setting may get better and quicker results than an all-out major, code-4 clinical reaction by treatment staff.

These are tough clinical calls, but someone has. to make them. Two heads make these decisions better than one, and a team will make them even better.

Postvention/Helping The Survivors Of Suicide

Suicide is a painful fact of life. Everybody prays it won't happen, but sometimes it does. And despite our best efforts. The following guidelines were developed by my agency to help surviving family members, staff, and other patients. While not appropriate for all settings, I've edited them in such a way as, I hope, may prove useful to you and yours.

To set the scene, it may be useful to think about a death by suicide as, simply, a traumatic event of such magnitude that those who knew the person (or patient) will likely experience sufficient emotional distress to develop those symptoms commonly found among trauma victims: depression; sadness; anger; shock; disbelief; recurrent and intrusive memories; dreams of the event; the sudden feeling as if the event were recurring; intense psychological distress at exposure to the scene or things that symbolize the death; avoidance of the scene, setting, or topic; diminished interest in life; detachment; restricted feelings; numbness; poor concentration; sleep disturbance; exaggerated startle response; and especially in suicide survivors, the experience of suicidal ideation.

These symptoms are, of course, those that make up the syndrome of Post Traumatic Stress Disorder and, as such, are easily recognized among survivors. They are also easily and effectively treated.

A suicide is traumatic to those closest to it for obvious reasons: It is sudden and unexpected, often violent, amounts to the worst kind of rejection for the survivors, and triggers all sorts of guilt and self-blame. There is, in my experience, no quickly getting over the suicidal death of anyone close to us—either as patient, colleague, friend, or family member. So, to survive a suicide at all we must remember something I wrote for a talk I gave to a survivors of suicide group in our community: It takes people to break our hearts, and it takes people to make them whole again.

Making Everyone Whole Again

If you are working in a provider agency, counseling center, clinic group private practice, or some such place, you have three groups of folks to take care of: immediate family, other patients who knew the suicide, and treatment staff who worked with the patient. If you are working in the schools, you have other things to worry about (see section under controlling contagion).

Family: Surviving family members are at the greatest risk of developing symptoms. There is, simply, no greater source of anguish than a death by suicide—especially if it is a child. Here are some helpful steps to take:

1) After a suicide, a supervisor (not the primary therapist or case manager unless this has been carefully discussed) should call the family and express condolences. An offer of further assistance can be made together with a promise to call a little later on. Families are usually in shock in the first few days after a suicide, so it is usually better to wait a couple weeks to offer additional support. This is, however, a judgment call. For example, if anyone in the family seems, appears, or is reported to be thinking or talking about suicide, don't wait, but intervene immediately.

2) On the second call, the family might be offered a no-fee visit to discuss the aftermath of the suicide—either in the home or at the agency. This may or may not be with the therapist who was treating their loved one. The decision here is a dicey one and depends on a number of things: how the therapist feels, how the family feels about him or her, and other such matters.

3) If contact with family survivors is made, this is the time to evaluate the presence of trauma symptoms and/or suicidality, and to make a referral for a support group or, in some cases, individual or family therapy.

4) While doing this work, it is strongly recommended the family not be blamed (even though one or more of

them may have unconsciously wished for the death), and that no suggestion be made that more could have been done (implication of negligence).

5) Whoever does this work had best be prepared for some anger, a possible threat of a lawsuit, and other such strong emotions as frequently accompany a sudden and unexpected loss of life. Most families, however, appreciate both the courage and the kindness.

6) The therapist and other staff who knew the patient should only attend the funeral on specific invitation; otherwise one's presence may oblige an introduction which could violate the deceased's privacy and/or make things awkward for the family.

7) However badly a therapist may wish to talk to the family, it is important that the family not be exposed to the therapist's pain and grief until it has remitted some; otherwise, the family may feel obliged to be of some help to the therapist and, thereby, may avoid dealing with its own grief.

Finally, it is my strong belief that since therapists often know a great deal more about the private hells their patients endured than their families did, what they learned in therapy should be kept confidential. Sometimes it is better that some secrets go to the grave with us.

Other Clients Or Patients

One patient's suicide, according to contagion theory, can create additional suicide risk in others. In a clinical setting, you already have people who have been suicidal, are considering suicide, or are suicide receptive (depressed and hopeless). Therefore, to minimize additional suicidal behaviors in those who knew the patient, or knew of the suicide, here are some steps to take:

1) Staff should be instructed to short-circuit rumors about the suicide. This can be done by containing the source of information, i.e, appointing one person as the single, authoritative person to whom others can go for answers.

2) Those who witnessed or know the details of a suicide should pass this information immediately up the lines of authority, thereby minimizing the risk of rumor.

3) If the suicide occurred on premises and was witnessed by other clients or staff, a meeting should be called immediately among the key players on the team to answer the following question: *Who is going to say what to whom?* With a single source authority on what information will be given to other clients, staff can be told, specifically, what to say to calm survivors down.

4) Staff should next identify those patients considered at special risk: those who knew the suicide, those who may have witnessed the death, those who may have known the suicide was imminent, the person who discovered the body, those in the same therapy group, and so on. These patients need to be outreached, given extra therapy time and put through a routine critical incident debriefing process that, as we all know, proves so psychologically helpful to any of us who've been heavily impacted by a traumatic event. According to the trauma experts, this special sensitivity and attention should be extended for at least 60 days.

5) Last, it is important to remember that not all other patients will be survivors (little identification with model, never knew him, etc.) and that, therefore, a

quick return to normal routine is best. This is not to suggest a "business-as-usual" attitude, but for most patients it is comforting and reassuring that services and programs not come to a sudden halt because someone suicided. Generally, staff may follow their own emotional barometers here about when to get back to normal.

Surviving Staff

No different in the pain and suffering department than anyone else, staff who lose a patient to suicide need special help. We experience all of the same emotions of other survivors—only sometimes, more so. After all, we were (like no one else) responsible for the well-being of the one who died. And as I've said elsewhere, we in the human services field can't afford to lose a single one of us. So let's be good to each other during this worst of all on-the-job tragedies. Here's how:

1) If you're an immediate supervisor and learn one of your staff has just had a suicide, drop what you're doing to go see him or her. If you're a supervisor once or twice removed up the line, wait a bit before dropping by—otherwise your arrival might be interpreted as the arrival of the Grand Inquisitor.

2) If you're a colleague, jump right in with emotional support. Your colleague has just suffered a severe blow to his or her professional identity and needs all the reassurance you can give. Young therapists and case managers need more, but old timers need support, too.

3) Remember that despite a sometimes overwhelming sense of guilt for failing the patient who died, quality

assurance reviews seldom find fault with the way a case was managed. The courts have been equally fair-minded and, in general, gross neglect is rarely present. It also helps to remember that suicide is multi-determined and that, despite our best efforts, the great majority of patients who die while in treatment were not suspected of being acutely suicidal by their treatment staff *at the time they suicided.*

4) If the suicide occurred in the context of a treatment team, the team should get together as soon as a meeting can be arranged, not only to support each other, but to put together a plan of action for the other survivors (family and fellow patients). Formal staff meetings on company time are highly recommended. Sometimes inviting in a respected staff member from another team (or even a mental health professional from outside the agency) can be most useful to this critical debriefing, grief-trauma work.

5) If there is to be a quality assurance review of the suicide, this work should be done by a disinterested third group of staff. Involved staff have neither the emotional wherewithal nor objectivity to carry out this mission.

> *Note:* It is sometimes the case that a suicide was not a suicide at all. Mental health staff are sometimes quick to assign the cause of death as suicide and, therefore, a coroner's report is needed to make this legal determination.

6) Last, supervisors should follow up with staff suicide survivors for at least a couple of months, checking for any persistent ideation, guilt, anger, or other unsettling emotions. They should be especially watchful for avoidance behavior, which generally takes the

following forms: being late for work, excessive absenteeism and, in particular, reluctance or refusal to work with suicidal patients. Sometimes a referral for therapy is indicated—lest the person eventually come to avoid the field of human services altogether.

One final suggestion: Following a suicide, any and all survivors may well experience a complicated bereavement. A fancy clinical term for the miserableness that often attends and persists after a suicide of someone we knew and cared about, it could just as well be called a haunting.

To get through this difficult time it is, I think, important to remember to take special care of ourselves. Nurture ourselves. Have a special meal. Sleep in late. Catch a good, uplifting movie. Go to a concert, a ballet, or whatever it is for us that is fine and light and wonderful and restores the joy of living.

The poet Tennyson wrote a line for all human service workers: "Never morning wore to evening, but some heart did break." When you decide to be involved in the lives of others, you get a special invitation to this heart-breaking business. My motto: Accept your grief, let it show, share it, and get and give a little help from your friends. Then be sure to go out and have a good time.

Psychosis

Psychoses are severe mental disturbances that may be chronic or short-lived. Typically, they are caused by some change in the organic and/or neurochemical functions of the brain. The causes of psychotic symptoms (hallucinations, delusions, racing thoughts, diminished impulse control, misinterpretation of reality, etc.) can range from acute drug or alcohol intoxication to head injuries to thoughts disordered by illnesses like schizophrenia. People experiencing psychotic symptoms concern us here because such patients are often at significant risk of ending their lives by suicide.

Here's the short course on psychosis and suicide:

1) People experiencing so-called "command hallucinations" to kill themselves (usually an authoritative, unpleasant, alien voice in their heads) are at extreme risk of suicide.

    Recommended action: an immediate consult with a mental health professional (preferably a psychiatrist); consideration of hospitalization; and any and all other interventions necessary to make the patient safe until treatments can be undertaken.

2) Young, intelligent people who have just learned they have what they now understand to be a life-long mental illness (e.g., schizophrenia, manic-depressive illness, etc.) often pass through a period of extreme suicide risk upon coming to this realization. Smart enough to realize what they have is an incurable mental illness, many of them suicide before they ever receive effective treatments.

    Recommended action: full disclosure of any and all relevant information about their diagnosis by a highly trained professional; family intervention and support; referral to an organization specifically designed to provide group, educational, respite, and rehabilitation support to the patient and his or her family.

In addition to materials at your local community mental health center, information about serious mental illness can be obtained from The National Alliance for the Mentally Ill or its state affiliates. Your mental health center will have the necessary numbers.

While some psychoses will pass with a period of detoxification and/or appropriate treatment, most of the chronic varieties can be effectively managed with modern anti-psychotic medications. The suicidal ideation associated with command hallucinations can, generally, be managed with a proper prescription and good patient compliance to a medical regime.

Those who work with the chronically mentally ill know too well that compliance (taking meds as prescribed) can sometimes be the biggest challenge to care givers. However, once an agreement to treatment is entered into and sustained over time, imminent suicide risk diminishes quickly.

Last, chronic mental illness is characterized by periods of relative stability punctuated by episodes of acute deterioration and dysfuntion, often triggered by ordinary life stressors, depression, and/or loss. It is during these acute episodes that suicidality needs to be assessed and re-assessed while special care is given to alleviate symptoms.

Rational Suicide/Right To Die

This is probably not the proper place to discuss so-called rational suicide. After all, this book was written with the idea of saving lives, not helping people end them. However, because of the interest in this topic, here's a brief summary of the subject together with some personal views.

The term "rational suicide" was coined by Jo Roman, a social worker who advocated choosing the time of one's death by actively bringing about that death. Ms. Roman personally took this action after receiving a diagnosis of breast cancer that would have, even in 1979, been treatable by a mastectomy. Notifying friends and family, she took her life with an overdose of pills. She left an educational video documentary of the whole affair as part of her legacy.

Since her passing, much talk, several books, dozens of national stories, and at least one best-seller have been written to promote the notion that, when your time finally comes and you've no way out, it should be all right with the society around you if you kill yourself. Or, even better, get an assist from a medical doctor.

This is a hot topic. And, given the increasingly high cost of extending life in patients with terminal conditions, it's one that is not going to go away. Some leaders are recommending that the major health care and mental health care professions must and should develop clear guidelines on the subject of "competence to commit suicide."

Historically, suicide has not always been wrong on the face of it. At different times, in different cultures, and among special classes of people, suicide has been quite acceptable. Therefore, given the reality of our climbing health care costs, the medical possibility of extending physical life well beyond what any "rational" person would want (or could afford), death with dignity campaigns will continue to flourish.

Already, straw and real ballots indicate the country is just about divided on the subject of the right to die. As the cost of care for the dying rises, AIDS takes even more people, and the whole subject of taking personal control of the end of one's life opens up for debate, my guess is the medical profession will gradually be permitted to step back from its life-at-any-cost position—a position some took, by the way, only after being sued for doing the humane thing for centuries. As well as they're paid and as much fun as medicine can be, I know some doctors who'd be happy to give up playing M.D. (Medical Deity) right now to avoid the whole looming controversy.

As a clinical psychologist, I have no special access to the truth in this matter, but it is my opinion that there may come a time for all of us when, caught in the medical reality of a terminal and perfectly inescapable, painful, costly, undignified condition, we might at least want the option to have a hand in our own final outcome. I think every rational, clear-thinking person at least wants this option—if only for him- or herself.

Having said this, I have great fears about not only a public debate of such things, but also about giving psychological license to those emotionally distraught people who, scanning the popular press, might be misled into believing suicide has now become an acceptable solution to one's problems.

Even more frightening is the active proposition and dissemination of the means and methods of suicide. With such information readily available in books like Derek Humphry's best seller, *Final Exit,* ambivalent suicidal people can now be assured a fairly certain death. This is not happy news to those of us who understand the nature of suicidal thinking and how little it takes to finally tip the scales of ambivalence in the direction of death.

Here, from a letter I received from a woman who read my other book *(Suicide: the Forever Decision),* is a quote which should give us all pause: "I've been thinking of suicide for some time now and the one thing holding me back is the thought of perhaps failing at the attempt. Are there really more failed attempts than completed suicides? I must be mighty stupid in not having the confidence in myself concerning taking my life. So many people indeed succeed. If I knew that I'd be successful in taking my life, I surely wouldn't be writing now, nor would I have read your book."

While still ambivalent about living or dying when she wrote me, she was also in therapy. Her suicide crisis was behind her and, like the great majority of physically healthy but momentarily depressed, demoralized, and disillusioned people who consider suicide, this woman wavered long enough to reach out to someone and save her own life. Had she read Mr. Humphry's book first, I wonder if I would have heard from her.

Risk Factors

The trouble with risk factors for suicide is that while everybody's got some, even those of us with a lot probably won't die by suicide. Suicide is simply too rare and complex a process for anyone to, at least today, correctly predict who will die by their own hand. Even in the highest risk groups, the death rate per 100,000 is not all that remarkable.

We know, for example, that suicide risk increases with age, is greater in Caucasian males who, because they are depressed and drinking excessively, have just been fired and, into the bargain, left by their wives. What all these risk factors don't tell us, however, is *which* intoxicated, depressed, old, just-fired, and separated white guys are going to kill themselves in the next 30 days. Or the next three hours. Or the next three years. At bottom, adding up risk factors won't tell us what we need to know *now*.

Consider the interplay of just some of the statistical risk factors studied thus far: age; sex; marital status; sexual orientation; ethnicity; religious affiliation; childhood loss; mental illness; physical illness; alcoholism; economic loss;

cumulative stressors of all sorts; biological factors; personality traits; family history and genetics; personal history with exposure to suicide models; and personal history of suicidal thinking and/or threats, gestures, and attempts.

Now consider the dynamic, often quite unpredictable, risk situations and contexts which may trigger suicidal behavior at any moment: an overwhelming sense of failure at some major task; an arrest which will produce terrible shame; the breakup of a cherished relationship; the accidental death of someone close; being thrown out of work because your company goes bankrupt; a wild fire which razes your home; a flood which washes your farm into the Gulf of Mexico; and last but not least, the only therapist you ever liked who has taken a job in a distant city on the same day your dog is backed over by the guy who was stealing your car after ripping off your TV.

Question: Does this man kill himself?

Answer: Probably not.

With so many individual risk factors to consider and so many contexts and circumstances that might prove suicidogenic for person A (but not for person B), is it any wonder we suicidologists are awash in a sea of data in search of decent theory?

One last point. Premature use of risk factors in clinical practice can be dangerous. For example, to the degree we use known risk factors to discount the suicidality of people in so-called low-risk groups, we put those people at an elevated risk in terms of our interventions and therapy. "She was just a teenager," I heard someone say once of a girl who had just taken her life with carbon monoxide. "Girls at that age only gesture."

Risk Management (Avoiding Malpractice)

Risk management is a business concept. As such, most good-hearted, well-intentioned clinicians, counselors, therapists, and other front line people helpers don't think too much about it. But they should. Even being accused of failing to make a good faith effort to intelligently manage the risk inherent in working with a suicidal client is painful. Having it proved in a court of law is positively the pits.

Here are some bad-news facts of our current reality:

- Lawsuits against people helpers are on a steep incline. The rate of filings against practitioners is climbing exponentially. Suicide is one of those areas where suits are increasing.

- With little protection from the law for this noble work, when someone dies tragically, our society starts looking for who did it. Since the victim is dead (and we often were the last people professionally involved), we are frequently blamed.

- Since we mental health professionals have increasingly advertised ourselves as able to cure mental illness and save lives, lawyers have increasingly been able to make us eat those words.

- Studies show that 50% of all suicides had a history of being in therapy.

- One suicide in six *is* in treatment at the time of the suicide.

  Note: The patient who suicides *does not have to still be in therapy* for you to be sued for malpractice. If a causal relationship between your action (or failure to act) can be proved, you're it.

- Studies also show that over an average career, half of all psychiatrists and one out of four or five psychologists will have a patient die by suicide.

- The once cozy fraternity of like-minded professionals who you could count on to help defend your actions in court no longer exists. If you are sued for malpractice, the plaintiff's lawyer can always find plenty of professionals with resumés longer than yours to nail your hide to the wall—even if you were a mostly good person who was only a little bit negligent.

Now here's the good news:

- Most claims for malpractice following a patient's death by suicide are thrown out of court and never come to trial.

- Even if a suit gets past the discovery phase (where all the facts are collected by the lawyers), and there is some merit to go forward, the great majority of cases settle out of court. You may not want to settle out of court (if you think you were right in your actions), but at this phase, your insurance company is less interested in your feelings than in containing costs and getting on with business.

- Except for licensed, registered professionals, other folks who try to stop or help a suicidal person are not likely to be successfully sued. In 1988, the California Supreme Court found that unlicensed counselors (clergy, scout leaders, college dormitory advisors, and others) have no duty to protect against potential harm to self. This doesn't mean someone can't sue you, but it does mean the suit is likely to be thrown out of court.

• Defending yourself against a malpractice suit is easier than you think. But you do have to *think*, and you do have to take to a few notes.

Before I outline what Allen Berman (a past president of the American Association of Suicidology and an expert on this subject) and others recommend on how to protect yourself from malpractice suits, let me say that the experience of being sued is uniformly unpleasant. Even winning will not take away the bad taste, hurt feelings, anger, and general rotten times you will have going through a lawsuit. As the French philosopher Rousseau once said, "I was ruined twice in my life; once when I lost a lawsuit, and once when I won one."

Therefore, my goal here is to keep you out of lawsuits altogether. While no substitute for proper legal counsel, here's how:

Background work:

1) Make sure you and everyone working with suicidal people in your agency, church, hospital, or school know the laws of your state governing how persons presenting a clear and present danger to themselves are to be managed. Laws vary, but many states now have specific requirements as to how people helpers are to act when a life is at stake. And make sure staff have read and understand these laws.

2) Make sure everyone knows the laws governing confidentiality and how these change when someone is at risk of suicide. The laws governing confidentiality vary tremendously, not only among states, but among agencies, service providers, and even professions. Therefore, when you have a suicidal person in your

care, you must be able to answer the question: Who else needs to know this person is in danger?

For example, in a recent Maryland case, school counselors who failed to tell a parent his child had made suicidal threats were found negligent when the child later killed herself. In other states where adolescent rights have greater protection, overriding them may lead to sanctions, or even a lawsuit.

3) If your agency has developed any in-house policies about how suicidal clients are to be handled (special procedures, required consultations, supervisory input, notifications of relatives, etc.), again, make sure all new (and old) employees are apprised of current policy.

> *Note:* If you have such procedures in place and nobody reads, knows, or follows them, don't even bother going to court—you're already finished.

4) If you don't now have one, an in-house suicide expert can be very helpful—provided, of course, all the staff know who he or she is, have been directed to use this expert in matters of acute or chronic suicide situations, and *use this person.*

If you don't have an in-house expert, consider getting someone from outside. Placing an outside suicide expert on your staff can prove very helpful in this consultant role. He or she is presumed not to be a part of any conspiracy to cover up what might have gone wrong and will, if ever called to court, make you look very good indeed. Besides giving staff a sense of increased security, you should get unbiased, less emotional advice on how to handle high risk situations.

(Put this person's name and number in the back of this book.)

5) An attorney of record with some mental health background can also prove very helpful in the role of consultant to your risk management program. (His or her name and number goes in the back of the book, too.)

6) If the agency has a library or resource room, it can be helpful for staff to have a section on suicide intervention and treatment. Staff can be referred to books, articles, and other professional literature on the subject and, in your defense, you have institutional proof positive that you take the subject of client suicide seriously.

> *Note:* If you are in solo or group private practice, taking any or all steps similar to the above will, generally, put you leagues ahead of the other practitioners currently operating in the private sector.

With this background work completed, you now have the everyday job of making sure suicidal people receive proper care and that such care is documented. "Proper care" is defined in part by the standards of care in your community, but also by the standards of care for your particular agency and profession. It is the standard of care, should you be sued for malpractice, against which your actions or inactions will be judged.

Maintaining a Standard of Care

The standard of care for suicidal people is not perfectly knowable. Standards change within professions, within the general treatments available and in terms of how society views what constitutes professional duty. Generally, malpractice suits following a patient's suicide are filed for the following reasons:

- The professional/agency failed to recognize the person was at risk. For example, liability has been imposed not only when the practitioner knew for certain an individual was suicidal, but when he or she "should have known" such person was at risk.

- The professional/agency did not take reasonable and prudent precautions to prevent the suicide once it was aware of the potential.

- Improper care. For example, if it was known the person was seriously depressed, were the customary treatments for depression considered and implemented? If not, why not? If the patient was an outpatient, was hospitalization considered? If not, why not?

You get the drift. Once suicidal risk has been established, the duty to do something reasonable and responsible is yours. The trick, now, is how to show a potential jury *just how reasonable and responsible you really are*.

Assuming you have done your homework and your agency, church, school, or office now has both the resources and the policies to provide a measure of safety and good treatment to suicidal people, all you have to do is prove it *IN WRITING*.

Frankly, here is where most of us fail. Simply put: no notes, no defense. Plaintiffs' lawyers simply love therapists who don't chart. Like Danish and coffee, they have them for breakfast. Since in the eyes of most juries we are presumed guilty when a patient dies by suicide, all the opposing lawyer has to prove is that not only were we stupid and negligent, but we didn't even care enough about what we were doing to bother writing it down.

It doesn't matter what we remember doing. It doesn't matter that we recall the patient promising she wouldn't take her life. It doesn't matter that we conducted a thorough assessment before making our decision not to hospitalize. It doesn't matter that we were too busy with a new crisis to chart the last one. What matters is what shows up in court as *fact*.

If the patient died and we didn't chart what we were thinking about, what factors we considered in our decision to not institute extraordinary measures, we are, *ipso facto*, guilty. And after being cross-examined for a couple of hours for failing to keep good records by an attorney skilled in medical malpractice you will, rather quickly, understand the joke that asks: If you are trapped in the bottom of deep malpractice pit with Saddam Hussein, a rattlesnake, and a lawyer, and have only two bullets in your gun, who do you shoot? Answer: The lawyer. Twice.

But you'd be wrong. Shooting lawyers is not the solution; they're just doing the best job they can for their clients. The one you should be angry with is you. Denial is a great defense mechanism, but denial of suicidal risk and the attendant professional responsibilities can cost you dearly.

To establish reasonable care, here are things you must do in a timely fashion:

1) Ask enough questions to establish suicide risk (at intake and ongoing).

2) Decide who in your agency is qualified to make such determinations. Senior staff? New staff? Students in training?

3)   Conduct other evaluations as necessary and/or appropriate. Psychological testing, Beck Inventories for Hopelessness and/or Depression, stress inventories, etc.

4)   If you routinely conduct mental status examinations, routinely conduct them on suicidal patients.

5)   If you routinely give patients a diagnosis (provisional or otherwise), do so with suicidal patients.

6)   If you routinely develop treatment plans, be sure you have a treatment plan for suicidal patients. Plans can include frequency of visits, modalities of treatment, consults, medications, lining up a hospital if necessary, etc.

> *Note:*   The specific content of a plan is less important than the fact that it proves you at least *thought* about what you were doing.

7)   If in doubt about suicidality, get a consult from an expert, a senior staff person, or a supervisor.

8)   Traditional therapeutic approaches hold up in court better than experimental ones. If the treatment was mainstream (no nudity, hot tubs, pyramid sitting, primal screaming, or any of the other weird stuff our profession seems to dream up), then you won't have a jury rolling its eyes while you try to explain why you were fooling around with voodoo therapy. (For what it's worth, it has always helped me to imagine my own mother sitting in the jury box.)

The guiding concept here is competent caring backed up by strong documentation. Competent caring includes, naturally, full adherence to ethical standards. Should you ever have a patient suicide after being exploited by a therapist in a sexual, financial, or even social dual relationship, just get out your checkbook because everything from that moment on is going quickly downhill.

It is also well to remember it is the little things we neglect to do that get us in the end. The phone call we didn't return because we were tired and wanted to get home; the spouse we were going to call to invite in for a session but didn't get around to; forgetting to arrange coverage when we were going to be out of town; and that consult we thought about getting but just never got around to. As professional misdemeanors none of these amount to much. But just wait until you have to defend them on a witness stand.

I'll end here with a few final notes:

1) It is just as important to show why *you did not do something* as it is to show you did something. If you decided not to hospitalize (medicate, get a consult, refer for medical evaluation, etc.), say why.

2) Your best defense is a good offense. Your best offense is a documented consultation from a senior staff person, psychologist, psychiatrist, or outside expert. If a second opinion about what action to take (or not take) is good, two second opinions are even better. Because later, in a court of law, it will then be three against one.

3) When you chart observations and progress notes, write or dictate histories and treatment plans (to later prove you were alert and taking nourishment while at work), try to imagine the following people hearing your words in a court of law: a judge, two or more lawyers, and a jury with your mother sitting in the front row. Imagining this audience should improve the quality of your written work at least two standard deviations.

4) When documenting suicidality on intake, or at any time during treatment, always write down the patient's commitment to safety. For example, "Yes, I won't hurt myself" or "No, I don't feel suicidal." *Quote the patient.* While the patient may still be thinking about suicide or feeling self-destructive, his or her own statement of safety and agreement to remain so will stand you in good stead if the worst happens.

5) Now then, repeat after me: Document. Document. Document.

Suicide Information & Education Centre (SIEC)

The SIEC is a computer-assisted resource library specifically designed and staffed for the purposes of maintaining all current print and audio visual materials on the subject of suicide. Located in Calgary, Alberta, Canada, SIEC is an excellent resource for those conducting research in the field, or for anyone needing the latest in information or educational materials for special projects, school programs, and the like. It also publishes a quarterly, the *SIEC Current Awareness Bulletin.* Contact the SIEC at 201-1615, 10th Ave. S.W., Calgary, Alberta, Canada, TSC 0J7. Phone: 403-245-0299.

Suicide Pacts

The most famous so-called suicide pact of recent times was that of four Bergenfield New Jersey youths who committed suicide together by locking themselves in a garage with the motor running in their car. At the time, March of 1987, their deaths received a great deal of attention in the media. Two days later, another pair of teenaged girls (some believe influenced by the pact deaths in New Jersey) also killed themselves by the same method.

For the record, when the lives of these young people were carefully examined for the years and months prior to their suicides, clear evidence of a host of troubles were found in the backgrounds of all those who died: drug abuse, dysfunctional families, school and relationship problems, and so on. The point is that suicide is always multi-determined and almost always much more complicated than newspaper stories can report. In my own view, no problem-free, psychologically healthy child joins a suicide pact—except, perhaps, in jest.

A suicide pact is an agreement between two or more people to take their lives by suicide. It is unknown how frequently this type of behavior occurs but, at least according to reports in the popular press, it seems more prevalent among the young and the old. Older couples faced with a frightening future have taken their own lives rather than travel down a road of increasing uncertainty, pain, and potential suffering.

Some theorists have pointed out that the elderly and the adolescent (where most so-called pact behavior occurs) have much in common psychologically: both face an uncertain future; both are undergoing a painful transition; both face real economic threats; both must deal with issues of unwanted dependency. To the degree those in these age groups are coping with the same problems, they are particularly susceptible to depression, helplessness, and hopelessness—all key precipitants for suicide.

With only very limited experience with pacts (and there seems to be very little published about them), here are three simple suggestions:

1) If working with young people, at least ask, "Who else knows about your wish to die?" Then, perhaps, "Do they want to die, too?"

2) No child in her right mind is going to tattle on pals, so if you get resistance, go directly to the other kid(s) you think *might* be involved.

3) For young couples so in love they've decided if they can't live together they must die together, the obvious suggestion is to split them up for interviews so the healthier one can join with you to call off the plan.

No matter how faithfully committed to a suicide pact everyone seems to be, at least one person in the pact would rather go see a Woody Allen movie. Find this person, make an approach and an appeal, and most likely, the rest can be saved. Social pressure to conform can be overwhelming, but it only works when the person being pressured has no option; give the person that option and he or she will be out of there in a minute.

Survivors Of Suicide

The survivors of suicide, just in America, are estimated to number into the thousands each year. If you assume that each suicide leaves behind at least six people who were emotionally close to the victim, and you multiply that figure by a conservative 30,000 suicides per year, then you have approximately 180,000 people seriously impacted by suicidal death each year. One preliminary study (which includes the suicidal deaths of aunts, uncles, cousins, and grandparents) suggests there may be as many as 27 million survivors in America alone.

The figure of those emotionally touched by suicidal behavior in a loved one (when you throw in threats, gestures, and attempts) becomes astronomical. Basically, no one escapes the effects of suicidal behavior in this society.

I have written elsewhere about what can be done to minimize the damaging effects of a recent suicide (see sections on contagion and postvention); here I would like to discuss the long-term business of being a suicide survivor and what might be done to ease the pain and enhance the healing of those left behind.

As a volunteer consultant to a suicide survivors' group, I would like to suggest the following:

- Every community that can sustain one should have a survivors of suicide self-help group. Such support groups can do what no professional can: provide a free, caring, non-judgmental, social environment in which people can come to share and grieve at their own pace.

- While such groups can be set up any number of ways, a professional consultant can sometimes prove very helpful. Your local mental health center might provide such a consultant.

- Where the grief of a survivor becomes debilitating, professional consultation is generally indicated— preferably with a therapist who specializes in grief work.

The best single source for information on survivor issues is the American Association of Suicidology. This organization provides technical assistance to survivor groups, publishes the quarterly newsletter, *Surviving Suicide,* and will gladly send along a complete listing of pamphlets, books, and bibliographies to help individuals, families, and groups learn more about the process. It also publishes a directory of SOS (survivors of suicide) support groups.

Because the nearest support group is often too far away to be of practical value for a survivor you may know or be working with, consider starting a group yourself—with or without a little help from your friends. The Association can and will direct you through the basics of getting a survivors' group started.

Among others, the actress Mariette Hartley (herself a survivor) is a strong supporter of this movement toward a better understanding of suicidal death and more compassion for its survivors. Support groups provide both a place to heal and a potential vehicle for community understanding that might lead, someday, to a de-stigmatization of suicide on a national scale. Such an enlightenment can't come too soon.

Threats

Suicide threats can take any of the following forms: verbal, behavioral, or written. Sometimes plain and straightforward, at other times they can be vague and difficult to interpret. The common message of a threat is a desire to die or kill oneself and, therefore, all threats should be taken seriously—at least until the true nature of the person's intent can be established.

Maybe the best way to think about suicide threats is as a form of interpersonal communication. Obvious, oblique, subtle, or blunt, the suicidal communiqué is usually between two people who know each other. Even a suicide threat made in jest should be examined for intent.

As written about elsewhere in the section on intervention, all communiqués that raise the idea of death, suicide, or self-harm in the mind of the recipient warrant a further inquiry into the real meaning. The despondent boy watching a religious show on television (much to his mother's delight since he's been in so much trouble at school lately), who asks, "Do you think God has a place for a boy like me?," is not saying he's just converted to Christianity; he's saying he wonders if dying wouldn't be better than living. (In this sad case, the mother didn't hear the message.)

My motto: If a suicide threat *sounds like* a suicide threat, it probably is. So why not check it out?

Victim-Precipitated Suicide

Once asked to work with a police officer who shot and killed a robbery suspect (I was seeing him for an acute post traumatic stress disorder and critical incident debriefing), I learned that the man the officer killed had done the following things: made no effort to conceal his identity in a small town where he was a known addict when he held up a drug store for morphine, and stuffed wads of newspaper into the chambers of his revolver so that it "appeared" loaded. When confronted and commanded three times to put down the weapon he was pointing at the police officer, he refused to do so and, instead, began to move forward with the pistol pointed directly at the officer. True to his training, the policeman did his duty.

In conducting an arm's-length psychological autopsy of the robber, his background bore all the signs and symptoms of suicidal erosion: fired from work, unemployed, family conflicts, wife about to divorce him, long-standing addiction to prescription and illicit drugs, depression, recent threats of suicide made to his family and friends, and, at last, commission of felony in broad daylight. He was also under the influence of the stolen drugs at the time the officer pulled him over.

The officer I was working with was, clearly, the victim of a suicide. The man he necessarily killed in the line of duty was seeking death but not, precisely, at his own hand. Rather, he used an innocent to accomplish his ends.

Victim-precipitated suicides can include such things as stepping in front of oncoming vehicles, lying down on a track in front of an approaching train, or stepping into a known off-duty policemen's tavern, pulling out a gun (even a toy gun will do) and shouting, "I'm a going to kill every pig in here!"

The tragedy of the victim-precipitated suicide is that not only does someone die by suicide, but the one who unwillingly does the killing is severely traumatized by the event. In high-speed traffic situations, or jumping from buildings and bridges into crowds of people or traffic, there may be even more related deaths or injuries. In my view, then, all such suspicious deaths should receive a psychological autopsy—not so much for the benefit of the deceased as for the psychological welfare of the living.

Youth (Under 15)

Although the data on suicide under the age of 15 are not at all good, there is some cause for alarm. Suicide completions for 10-to-14 year-olds are up and, more and more, child mental health specialists are dealing with younger and younger kids who are thinking and talking about suicide. As the leading reason for child psychiatric emergencies across the country, suicide is no longer an esoteric subject for those dealing with the very young.

Among experts there is some reason to question whether, in fact, children under the age of 10 can truly conceptualize death and the finality of that condition and, therefore, form an intent to die. Still, young people take trips to places they've never been before all the time. To the degree suicide and death are portrayed as adventures, escapes, and solutions to the frustrations of life on television and in the movies, none of us can afford to casually dismiss the suicidal thoughts, threats, gestures, or attempts in the very young.

Maybe only a suicidologist would notice, but when I saw the remake of Peter Pan recently and observed that Dustin Hoffman, in the role of Hook, points a pistol to his head and begins chanting, "You can't stop me. You can't stop me. You can't stop me. Stop me. Stop me. Stop me!," he is modeling two of the classic themes of suicide: ambivalence about dying, and how suicide is a solution to problems. In Hook's case, with an aging Peter Pan no longer a worthy opponent, the problem is, "What's a pirate to do when there are no more adventures?"

My point here is that the millions of little kids (10 and under) who saw this movie were, at minimum, exposed to a suicide model—complete with a visual aid about what part of one's anatomy to point a loaded pistol. Despite any misgivings we may have, it seems there is no way possible to keep children innocent about the subject of suicide, or the fact that it is portrayed by many as a way to solve life's problems.

Given this fact of life, then, maybe the best thing we can do when we suspect a child may be thinking about self-destruction is to just go ahead and ask. If we get a "yes," then maybe it's time to sit down and have a long talk about living life, or get a consult from a child mental health specialist. But one thing seems sure: Kids have to grow up much too quickly these days. I know this to be a fact because the last time I went there, they didn't need a child psychiatrist in Never Never Land.

References and Readings

• • •

REFERENCES

Berman, A.L. & Jobes, D.A. *Adolescent suicide: assessment and intervention.* Washington, DC: American Psychological Association, 1991.

Beck, A.T., Weissman, A., Lester, D., & Trexler, L. The measurement of pessimism: The Hopelessness Scale. *Journal of Consulting and Clinical Psychology.* 1974, 42, 861-865.

Berlin, Irving, N. Suicide among American Indian adolescents: An overview. *Suicide & Life-Threatening Behavior.* 1987, 17: 218-233.

Bonger, B. *The suicide patient: Clinical and legal standards of care.* Washington, DC: American Psychological Association, 1996.

Blumenthal, S.J. & Kupfer, D.J. (Eds.). *Suicide over the life cycle: Risk factors, assessment, and treatment of suicidal patients.* Washington, DC: American Psychiatric Press, 1990.

Centers for Disease Control. CDC recommendations for a community plan for the prevention and containment of suicide clusters. MMWR, 1986, 37 (suppl. no. S-6).

Gibbs, J.T. Conceptual, methodological, and sociocultural issues in African-American youth suicide: Implications for assessment and early intervention. *Suicide & Life-Threatening Behavior.* 1988, 18: 73-89.

Hawton, K. *Suicide and attempted suicide among children and adolescents.* Newbury Park, CA: Sage, 1986.

Fowler, R.C., Rich, C.L. & Young, D. San Diego suicide study. II. Substance abuse in young cases. *Archives of General Psychiatry.* 1986, 43: 962-965.

Menninger, K. *Man against himself.* New York: World Book, 1938.

Murphy, G.E. & Wetzel, R.D.L. The lifetime risk of suicide in alcoholism. *Archives of General Psychiatry.* 1990, 47: 383-392.

Phillips, D.P. & Wills, J.S. A Drop in Suicides around Major National Holidays. *Suicide & Life-Threatening Behavior.* The American Association of Suicidology, Spring 1987, 17: 1.

Quinnett, P., *Suicide: The Forever Decision.* The Continuum Publishing Co., New York, 1989.

Richman, J. *Family therapy for suicidal people.* Springer Publishing Company, New York, 1986.

Sorenson, S. B. & Golding, J.M. Prevalence of suicide attempts in a Mexican-American population: prevention implications of immigration and cultural issues. *Suicide & Life-Threatening Behavior.* 1988, 18: 322-333.

Sorenson, S.B. & Rutter, C.M. Transgenerational patterns of suicide attempt. *Journal of Consulting and Clinical Psychology.* 59, 861-866.

Takahashi, Y. Suicidal Asian patients: recommendations for treatment. *Suicide & Life-Threatening Behavior.* 1989, 19: 305-313.

World Health Organization, Regional Office for Europe. Suicidal behavior among people with HIV and AIDS. *Report on WHO Consultation.* W.H.O., Copenhagen, 1990.

READINGS IN ETHNIC ISSUES

Munoze, F.U. & Endo, R. (Eds.). *Perspectives in Minority Group Mental Health.* United Press of America, Inc. Washington, D.C., 1982.

Gibbs, J.T., Huang, L.N. & Associates. *Children of Color: Psychological Interventions with Minority Youth.* Jossey-Bass, San Francisco, 1989.

Dana, R.H. (Ed.). *Human Services for Cultural Minorities.* University Park Press, Baltimore, 1981.

Chunn, J.C., Dunston, P.J. & Ross-Sheriff, T. *Mental Health and People of Color: Curriculum Development and Change.* Howard University Press, Washington, D.C., 1983.

GENERAL READINGS (PUBLISHERS NOT LISTED)

Alverez, A. *The savage god; a study of suicide*, 1972.

Giffin, M. *A cry for help*, 1983.

Grollman, E.A. *Suicide: Prevention, Intervention, Postvention*, 1971.

Hendin, H. *Black suicide*, 1969.

Hendin, H. *Suicide in America*, 1982.

Hyde, M. *Suicide: the hidden epidemic*, 1978.

Jacobs, J. *Adolescent suicide*, 1971.

Klagsborn, F. *Too young to die*, 1976.

Maris, R.W. *Pathways to suicide: a survey of self-destructive behaviors*, 1981.

Shneidman, E.S. *Deaths of man*, 1973.

Wekstein, L. *Handbook of Suicidology: principles, problems, and practice*, 1979.

SUICIDE PREVENTION SUPPORT SYSTEM

● ● ●————————————————————————● ● ●

911
In-House Security _____
Hospital Emergency Room _____
Local Crisis Line _____
Poison Control Center _____
Local Mental Health Numbers _____
_____
_____
_____
_____

Supervisor's Home Number _____
Director's Home Number _____
Consultants/Backup Personnel _____
_____

Referrals (Practitioners/Therapists) _____
_____
_____
_____

Child & Adolescent Specialist _____
Geriatric Specialist _____
Family Systems Therapist _____

Drug & Alcohol Specialists _____

Interpreters (Deaf, Spanish, Hmong, Etc.) _____
_____
_____
_____

Attorney _____
Suicide Survivors Group _____
American Association of Suicidology _____

To order additional books, check desired titles and designate number of copies. All but the last title are paperbacks. Send check or money order (U.S. funds only) to:

C-Books • 601 S. Division • Spokane, WA 99202

	Copies	Amount

☐ *When Self-Help Fails. A Guide to Counseling Services.* ($12.95)

☐ *Suicide: The Forever Decision.* For Those Thinking About Suicide, And For Those Who Know, Love, Or Counsel Them. ($9.95)

☐ *Suicide: Intervention and Therapy.* Undoing the Forever Decision. ($14.95)

☐ *On Becoming a Health and Human Service Manager. A Practical Guide for Clinicians and Counselors.* ($19.95)

☐ **Check here if you would like books autographed.**

                                 sub total

1) Subtract 10% on purchase of 3-5 books; 20% on 6-9 books; 30% on 10 or more books. 1) ____
2) Add $3.00 shipping and handling fee to all orders. 2) ____
3) Washington residents add 8% sales tax. 3) ____

Total ____

Please send information on workshops!
☐ Suicide Intervention and Therapy
☐ Management-Clinician & Counselor

Ship to: **Name** _____
         Company _____
         Address _____
         City/State/Zip _____